TWILIGHT PRAYERS
Sloka Work Book

JET Publishing House

INDIA   USA

TOWARDS EXCELLENCE

P
R
A
J
N
A

Title	Twilight Prayers
Subtitle	Sloka Work Book
Copyright	Jeeyar Educational Trust
First Edition	2011
Contributor	His Holiness Chinna Jeeyar Swamiji

CONTACT US:

INDIA

JIVA
Sriramanagaram, Shamshabad,
R.R. Dist. Andhra Pradesh - 509 325
Phone: 95535 49971, 95535 499

UNITED STATES

JETUSA Inc.
Jeeyar Asram, 222, Dey Road,
CRANBURY, NJ 08512, USA
Phone:609-297-8797

Website: www.prajna4me.org   **Email:** prajna@jetusa.org

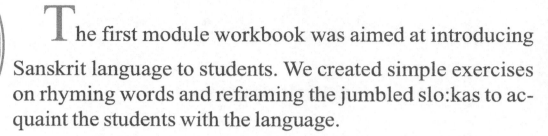

A WORD
Jai Srimannarayana!

The first module workbook was aimed at introducing Sanskrit language to students. We created simple exercises on rhyming words and reframing the jumbled slo:kas to acquaint the students with the language.

In the second module, our focus is on introducing the students with the meaning of words and their usage. The words used were picked from the slo:kas. Additional similar words were selected and exercises were formed for better understanding.

In Sanskrit, there are two categories of words

- Subanthas – Nouns, pronouns, adjectives, fall under this category. Propositions make these words meaningful.

- Thiganthas – Verbs and adverbs fall under this category. There are 10 types of tenses such as present tense, past tense, etc; which make these words meaningful.

While teaching Sanskrit professionally, all these seven cases and tenses are taught in a tabular form. Now, we are not going to delve deep into it.

As students are already introduced to a few tenses and propositions through slokas, we felt children would be interested in trying to experiment with the new vocabulary. To satisfy their curiosity, we prepared exercises in attractive formats.

For a student to enjoy the activities presented in this book, it is mandatory for the teachers to initially acquaint themselves with the material, to understand and practice the exercises before teaching.

Some outreach projects have also been added in every lesson keeping in view that these Prajna students will involve themselves in the community services to evolve their personality and also to become good citizens. Our intention is for our students to achieve multi dimensional growth and all our efforts and exercises are based on this thought.

This is a maiden attempt of the Prajna committee. We invite you to render your part of service by sending us your valuable suggestions.

Sriramnagar
8 July 2012

PRAJNA PLEDGE

Jai Srimannarayana!

O Mother Earth! I, being your best child and responsible citizen of this world, take this pledge!

I shall revere my parents, my family, my Gurus and treat everyone with love.

I shall serve my community, my country and those in need.

I pledge to protect the Nature by caring for animals, trees and the environment.

I will learn from the experiences of my ancestors and pass it on to future generations.

I, as student of Prajna, swear to abide by the universal commandments -

Worship your own and Respect all &
Serve all beings As service to God.

Jai Srimannarayana!

Table of Contents

Telugu	Hindi	English	Telugu	Hindi	English
అ	अ	a	ట	ट	ta
ఆ	आ	a:	ట్ట	ट्ट	tta
ఇ	इ	i	ఠ	ठ	**tta**
ఈ	ई	i:	డ	ड	**da**
ఉ	उ	u	డ్డ	ड्ड	**dda**
ఊ	ऊ	u:	ఢ	ढ	**dha**
ఋ	ऋ	ru	ణ	ण	**na**
ౠ	ॠ	ru:	త	त	tha
ఌ	अलु	lu	త్త	त्त	ththa
ౡ	अलू	lu:	థ	थ	ttha
ఎ		e	ద	द	da
ఏ	ए	e:	ద్ద	द्द	dda
ఐ	ऐ	ai	ధ	ध	dha
ఒ		o	న	न	na
ఓ	ओ	o:	ప	प	pa
ఔ	औ	au/ow	ఫ	फ	pha
అం	अं	am	బ	ब	ba
అః	अः	aha	భ	भ	bha
క	क	ka	మ	म	ma
ఖ	ख	kha	య	य	ya
గ	ग	ga	ర	र	ra
ఘ	घ	gha	ల	ल	la
ఙ	ङ	nga	వ	व	va
చ	च	cha	శ	श	sa
చ్చ	च्च	chcha	ష	ष	sha
ఛ	छ	chha	స	स	sa
ఛ	छ	chha	హ	ह	ha
జ	ज	ja	ళ	ळ	la
ఝ	झ	jha	ఱ		rra
ఞ	ज	ini	క్ష	क्ष	ksha
			జ్ఞ		Jna

- ● This letter comes only in the middle of the word
- ● ●This letter comes in the beginning/middle of the word
- 👉 Pronounciation of both these letters is almost similar

1. Haryashtakam

harir harathi pa:pa:ni dushta chiththai rapi smruthaha I
anichchaya:pi samsprushto: dahathye:vahi pa:vakaha II

sa ganga: sa gaya: se:thuhu sa ka:si: sa cha pushkaram |
jihva:gre: varthathe: yasya   hari rithyakshara dvayam || 1

va:ra:nasya:m kurukshe:thre: naimisa:ranya e:va cha |
yath krutham the:na ye:no:ktham hari rithyakshara dvayam || 2

prutthivya:m ya:ni thi:rttha:ni punya: nya:ya thana:ni cha |
tha:ni sarva:nya se:sha:ni hari rithyakshara dvayam || 3

gava:m ko:ti sahasra:ni he:ma kanya: sahasrakam |
daththam sya:ththe:na ye:no:ktham hari rithyakshara dvayam || 4

rugve:do:ttha yajur ve:daha sa:ma ve:do: pyattharvanaha |
adhi:thasthe:na ye:no:ktham hari rithyakshara dvayam || 5

asvame:dhair maha:yajnyaihi nara me:dhai sthatthaiva cha |
ishtam sya:ththe:na ye:no:ktham hari rithyakshara dvayam || 6

pra:na praya:na pa:tthe:yam samsa:ra vya:dhi na:sanam |
dukha: thyantha parithra:nam hari rithyakshara dvayam || 7

baddhah parikarasthe:na mo:ksha:ya gamanam prathi |
sakrud uccha:ritham ye:na hari rithyakshara dvayam || 8

haryashtakam idam punyam pra:thar uttha:ya yah patte:th |
a:yushyam balam aro:gyam yaso: vruddhis sriya:vaham ||

prahla:de:na krutham stho:thram duhkha sa:gara so:shanam |
yah patte:th sa naro: ya:thi thad vishno:h paramam padam ||

2. Krushna:shtakam

vasude:va sutham de:vam kamsa cha:nu:ra mardanam I
de:vaki: parama:nandam krushnam vande: jagad gurum II   1

athasi: pushpa samka:sam ha:ra nu:pura so:bhitham I
rathna kankana ke:yu:ram krushnam vande: jagad gurum II   2

kutila:laka samyuktham pu:rna chandra nibha:nanam I
vilasath kundala dharam krushnam vande: jagad gurum II   3

manda:ra gandha samyuktham cha:ru ha:sam chathur bhujam I
barhi pinchha:va chu:da:ngam krushnam vande: jagad gurum II   4

uthphulla padma pathra:ksham ni:la ji:mu:tha sannibham I
ya:dava:na:m siro:rathnam krushnam vande: jagad gurum II   5

rukmini: ke:li samyuktham pi:tha:mbara suso:bhitham I
ava:ptha thulasi: gandham krushnam vande: jagad gurum II   6

go:pika:na:m kucha dvandva kumkuma:nkitha vakshasam I
sri:nike:tham mahe:shva:sam krushnam vande: jagad gurum II   7

sri:vathsa:nkam maho:raskam vanama:la: vira:jitham I
sankha chakra dharam de:vam krushnam vande: jagad gurum II   8

hala sruthi

krushna:shtakam idam punyam pra:tha ruttha:ya yah patte:th I
ko:ti janma krutham pa:pam smarane:na vinasyathi II   9

---

3. Pancha:yudha Stho:thram

sphurath sahasra:ra sikha:thi thi:vram

  sudarsanam bha:skara ko:ti thulyam |

surad visha:m pra:na vina:si vishno:ho

  chakram sada:ham saranam prapadye: || 1

vishno:r mukho:ttha:nila pu:rithasya

  yasya dhvanir da:na vadarpa hantha: |

tham pa:ncha janyam sasi ko:ti subhram

  sankham sada:ham saranam prapadye: || 2

hiranmayi:m me:ru sama:na sa:ra:m

  koumo:daki:m daithya kulaika hanthri:m I

vaikuntta va:ma:gra kara:bhimrishta:m

 gada:m sada:ham **sara**n**am** prapadye: II   3

raksho:sura:**na**:m kattino:gra kantta

 chche:dakshara chcho:**n**itha digdha dha:ram I

tham nandakam na:ma hare:h pradi:ptham

 khadgam sada:ham **sara**n**am** prapadye: II   4

Yajjya:ni na:da **sravana**:th sura:**na**:m

 che:tha:msi nirmuktha bhaya:ni sadyaha I

bhavanthi daithya:sani ba:**na** varshi

 sa:r**n**gam sada:ham **sara**n**am** prapadye: II   5

Phala sruthi

imam hare:h pancha maha:yudha:na:m

 sthavam patte:th yo:nudinam prabha:the: I

samastha duhkha:ni bhaya:ni sadyaha

 pa:pa:ni na**s**yanthi sukha:ni santhi   II   6

vane: ra**n**e: **s**athru jala:gni madhye:

 yadruchcha ya:pathsu maha: bhaye:shu I

idam pattan stho:thra mana:kula:thma:

 sukhi: bhave:th thathkrutha sarva rakshaha II   7

sa **s**ankha chakram sa gada:si **s**a:r**n**gam

 pi:thambaram kausthubha vathsa chinham I

sriya: same:tho:jjvala so:bhitha:ngam

    vishnum sada:ham saranam prapadye: II   8

jale: rakshathu va:ra:haha stthale: rakshathu va:manaha I

atavya:m na:rasimhascha sarvathaha pa:thu ke:savaha   II   9

4. Gaje:ndra Mo:kshanam

gra:ha grasthe: gaje:ndre:, rudathi sarabhasam tha:rkshya ma:ruhya dha:van,

vya:ghu:rnan ma:lya bhu:sha: , vasana parikaro: me:gha gambhi:ra gho:shaha I

a:bibhra:no: rattha:ngam, saramasi mabhayam sankha cha:pau sakhe:tau,

hasthaih kaumo:daki: mapyavathu hari rasau, amhasa:m samhathe:rnaha II

nakra:kra:nthe: kari:ndre: mukulitha nayane: mu:la mu:le:thi khinne:,

na:ham na:ham na cha:ham, na cha bhavathi puna stha:druso: ma:druse:shu |

ithye:vam thyaktha hasthe:, sapadi suragane: bha:va su:nye: samasthe:

mu:lam yath pra:dura:si:th sa disathu bhagava:n mangalam santhatham naha ||

5. Slo:ka Thrayam

pra:tha ssmara:mi bhava bhi:thi maha:rthi sa:nthyai

na:ra:yanam garuda va:hana manjana:bham   I

gra:ha:bhi bhu:tha mada va:rana mukthi he:thum

chakra:yudham tharuna va:rija pathra ne:thram   II   1

pra:thar nama:mi manasa: vachasa: cha mu:rdhna:

pa:da:ravinda yugalam paramasya pumsaha   I

na:ra:yanasya naraka:rnava tha:ranasya

pa:ra:yana pravana vipra para:yanasya   II   2

pra:thar bhaja:mi bhajatha:m abhayankaram tham

pra:k sarva janma krutha pa:pa bhaya:panuthyai |

yo: gra:ha vakthra pathitha:nghri gaje:ndra gho:ra

so:ka prana:sana karo: dhrutha sankha chakraha || 3

Phala sruthi

slo:ka thrayam idam punyam pra:thar uttha:ya yah patte:th   I

lo:ka thraya gurus thasmai dadya:d a:thma padam harihi   II   4

6. Parathva:di Panchakam

udyad bha:nu sahasra bha:svara para vyo:ma:spadam, nirmala

jna:na:nanda ghana svaru:pa m amala jna:na:dibhi sshad gunaihi |

jushtam, su:ri jana:dhipam, dhrutha rattha:nga:bja:di bhu:sho:jjvalam

sri: bhu: se:vyam anantha bho:gi nilayam sri:va:sude:vam bhaje: || 1

a:mo:de bhuvane: pramo:da utha sammo:de: cha sankarshanam,

pradyumnam cha thattha: niruddha mapitha:n samha:ra srushti stthith:hi |

kurva:na:n mathi mukhya shad gunavarair yuktha:n sthri yugma:thmakaiahi

vyu:ha:ddhishttitha va:sude:va mapitha:m kshi:ra:bdhi na:ttham bhaje: || 2

ve:da:nve:shana, mandara:dri bharana, kshmo:ddha:rana prasritha

prahla:da:vana bhu:mi bhikshana jagad vikra:nthayo: yathkriya:ha |

dushta kshathra nibarhanam, dasa mukha: dyunmu:lanam, karshanam

kalindya: athipa:pa kamsa nidhanam yath kri:ditham tham numaha || 3

yo: de:va:di chathur vidhe:shu janishu bramha:nda ko:sa:nthare:

sambhakthe:shu chara:chare:shu cha visan a:sthe: sada:nthar bahihi |

vishnus tham nikhile:shvanu shvanutharam bhu:yassu bhu:yastharam

sva:ngushtta pramitham cha yo:gi hrudaye:shu a:si:na mi:sam bhaje: || 4

sri:rangastthala ve:nkata:dri karigirya:dau sathe:shto:ththare:

sttha:ne: gra:ma nike:thane:shu cha sada: sa:nnidhya ma:se:dushe: |

archa:ru:pina marchaka:bhimathithas svi:kurvathe: vigraham

pu:ja:m cha:khilava:nchhitha:n vitharathe: sri:sa:ya thasmai namaha ||

5

Phala sruthi

pra:thar vishno:h parathva:di panchakasthuthim uththama:m |

pattan pra:pno:thi bhagavad bhakthim varada nirmitha:m ||

7. Parama:rttha Slo:ka Dvayam

sathsanga:th bhava nisspruho: guru mukha:th sri:sam prapadya:thmava:n,

pra:rabdham paribhujya karma sakalam prakshi:na karma:ntharaha |

nya:sa:de:va nirankuse:svara daya: nirlu:na ma:ya:nvayo:,

ha:rda:nugraha labdha madhya dhamani dva:ra:th bahir nirgathaha ||

1

muktho:rchirdina pu:rva paksha shad udang

     ma:sa:bda va:tha:msumath,

glau vidhyuth varune:ndra dha:thru mahithaha

     si:ma:ntha sindhva:pluthaha |

sri:vaikunttam upe:thya nithyam ajadam

     thasmin para bramhanaha,

sa:yujyam samava:pya nandathi samam

     the:naiva dhanyah puma:n ||

2

hala sruthi

pra:thar nithya:nu sandhe:yam parama:rttham mumukshubhihi |

slo:ka dvaye:na samkshiptham suvyaktham varado:bravi:th ||

Sarana:gathi

A Word of Submission

:m bhagavan na:ra:yana:bhimatha:nu ru:pa   swaru:pa ru:pa

una vibhavaiswarya   si:la:dyanavadhika:thi8888saya

sankhye:ya kalya:na guna gana:m,

adma vana:laya:m, bhagavathi:m,

riyam, de:vi:m, nithya:napayini:m, niravadya:m,

e:va de:va divya mahishi:m,

khila jagan ma:tharam,

sman ma:tharam, asaranya saranya:m,

nanya saranas sarana maham prapadye: //

1. Introduction

I. **Choose the correct answer**

1. When sa:thvik guna dominates, the person is

   a) angry

   b) pleasant

   c) lazy

   d) sleepy

2. When rajo:guna dominates, the person is

   a) selfish

   b) sleepy

   c) happy

   d) passive

3. When thamo:guna dominates, the person is

   a) pleasant

   b) friendly

   c) active

   d) passive

II. **Match the following**

sathva guna

rajo:guna

thamo:guna

III. Fill in the blanks

1. Divine twilight prayers are called _____.

2. _____ _____ are chanted early morning.

3. Twilight prayers help us realize our _____ and our relationship with _____.

4. To keep our knowledge in awakened state, man needs _____ state of mind.

IV. Answer the following

1. What are the three guna:s?

   _____

2. How does one behave when sa:thvik guna dominates ?

   _____

3. How is one identified as a ra:jasik person?

   _____

4. How can we develop sa:thvik nature?

   _____

5. List atleast five drawbacks of thamo:guna?

   _____

6. How do prayers help us?

   _____

Do You Know?

Each color has a significance as per our scriptures.

white   - sa:thvik
dark red   - ra:jasik
black   - tha:masik
green   - prosperity/abundance
pink   - love
yellow   - auspiciousness
blue   - divinity/ infiniteness/compassion

V. Identify the sa:thvik, ra:jasik, tha:masik creatures in the picture below. Color sa:thvik in pink, ra:jasik in red, and tha:masik in black color.

VI. Identify the sa:thvik, ra:jasik and tha:masik activities in the picture below
   Circle sa:thvik in green, ra:jasik in red, and tha:masik in black color.

VII. **Identify the sa:thvik, ra:jasik and tha:masik dresses in the picture below. Circle sa:thvik in pink, ra:jasik in red, and tha:masik in black color.**

VIII. Identify the sa:thvik, ra:jasik and tha:masik foods below. Circle sa:thvi
foods in yellow, ra:jasik foods in red, and tha:masik foods in black color

Haryashtakam

2. Haryashtakam

I. Choose the correct answer

1. Haryashtakam describes the unparalleled greatness of
    a) Lord Hari
    b) activities of Lord Hari
    c) word 'Hari' itself
    d) five weapons of Lord Hari

2. Va:rana:si is very sacred because
    a) Lord Krushna revealed Bhagawad Gi:tha here
    b) the most ancient temple of Lord Siva is here
    c) Lord Siva chants Ra:ma na:ma continuously thus purifying whol
       place
    d) all of the above

3. 'HARI' when chanted, cleanses us of all inner impurities as
    a) pure water cleanses the dirt
    b) clean air eliminates bad odor
    c) fire burns anything into ashes
    d) all of the above

4. The easiest way to get rid of inner impurities is by
    a) taking a dip in river Ganges
    b) visiting holy places
    c) simply chanting Hari na:ma
    d) visiting the Nala bridge

5. Chanting Hari na:ma is as auspicious as
    a) donating 10 million cows in charity
    b) conducting marriages of 1000s of girls decorated with gol
       ornaments
    c) visiting holy places
    d) all of the above

6. Greatness of Kurukshe:thra:

    a) enriches the right qualities in people

    b) Lord Krushna revealed Bhagawad Gi:tha here

    c) Maha:bha:ratha war took place

    d) all of the above

7. Get the benefit of chanting Ve:da:s by _____ instead.

    a) reading Pura:na:s

    b) eating prasa:dam

    c) chanting 'Hari' with devotion

    d) all of the above

8. Chanting Hari na:ma will give

    a) good health

    b) wealth

    c) fame & prosperity

    d) all of the above and much more

9. Who is as sacred as river Ganga:?

    a) One who chants na:ma Hari

    b) One who takes bath in Ganga: river

    c) One who gives alms to the poor

    d) One who constructs many temples

10. Gaya:

    a) pleases ancestors

    b) has many temples in it

    c) has lot of population

    d) all the rivers flow through this place

II. Fill in the blanks

1. _____ wipes off the sins.

2. Chanting Haryashtakam can dry up one's sins that are unlimited like a va[
   _____.

3. Ve:da:s are classified into _____ parts.

4. Chant 'Hari' at least _____ times every morning.

III. Match the following

he:ma

pa:vakaha

1000

jihva:

pra:thaha

sahasra

sakruth

IV. Complete the following words

1. p___d___m

2. kr___t___am

3. g___va:___

4. pra:___ ___

5. b___ l___m

V. Fill in the slo:ka blanks

1. pra:**na** praya:**na** _____

2. _____ vya:dhi na:**s**anam

3. _____ akshara dvayam

4. _____ se:thus saka:**s**i: sacha pushkaram

5. _____ parikaras the:na _____ gamanam prathi

VI. Rearrange the words to reveal the slo:ka

1. parikaraha	2. gamanam	3. mo:ksha:ya	4. the:na
5. baddhaha	6. prathi	7. ye:na	8. akshara
9. dvayam	10. ithi	11. uccha:ritham	12. sakruth
13. harihi			

VII. Circle the odd man out

1. Hari, Krushna, Sri: Lakshmi, Ra:ma, Vishnu,

2. greed, selfishness, wickedness, jealousy, righteousness

3. Yamuna, Saraswathi, Kurukshe:thra, Ganga:, Pushkara

4. tree, fire, air, water, land, space

5. Gi:tha, Va:rana:si, Pura:na:s, Ve:da:s

6. grief, sorrow, happiness, distress

7. sathvaguna, rajo:guna, duhkha, thamo:guna

8. Va:lmi:ki, Na:rada, Annama:cha:rya, Ve:da Vya:sa

VIII. Analogy

1. Ganga is to river as Naimisa:ranya is to _____

2. Nalase:thu is to bridge as Pushkaram is to _____

3. Sa:ma is to Ve:da as Aswame:dha is to _____

4. Haryashtakam is to Prahla:da as Bhagawad Gi:tha is to _____

5. Kurukshe:thra is to Bhagawad Gi:tha as _____ is to Pura:na:s

6. Ganga: is to purity as Ka:si: is to _____

7. Nalase:thu is to strength as Gaya: is to _____

8. Ashtakam is to _____ as dvayam is to _____

9. Prahla:da is to Na:rada as Pa:ndava:s is to _____

10. *Ha* is to bring out sins as *Ri* is to _____

11. Haryashtakam is to Hari as Krushna:shtakam is to _____

12. Sathvaguna is to happiness as Rajo:guna is to _____

13.   Prahla:da is to ra:kshasa as Hanuman is to _____

14.   Hari na:ma is to morning as _____ is to night.

IX. One word answers

1.   How many slo:kas does an "ashtakam" contain?

_____

2.   Who composed Haryashtakam?

_____

3.   When should we chant this stho:thra?

_____

4.   What is the root cause of all grief?

_____

5.   How many times does 'HARI' appear in this stho:thra?

_____

6.   Which sacred place has two different names?

_____

X. Answer the following

1.   Name the holy places.

_____

2.   What is the benefit of chanting Haryashtakam?

_____

3.   What is the message conveyed by Prahla:da ?

_____

XI. **Number the jumbled pictures as per the order of slo:kas, label them and wri**
the first word of the slo:ka

XII. Learn about Groups

The suffix 'kam' means an object which has a few items in it.

dvikam is

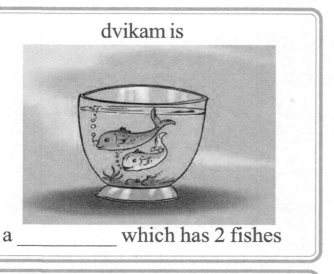

a _____ which has 2 fishes

dwayam means

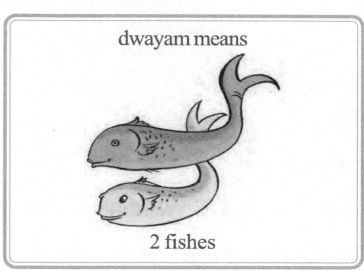

2 fishes

thrikam is

a _____ which has 3 monkeys

thrayam means

_____ monkeys

Starting from group of four 'kam' is used to identify object that has few items in it or the items itself

chathushkam is

a _____ with 4 books

chathushkam means

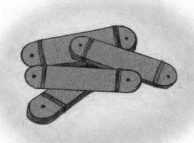

_____ books

Now complete the rest

panchakam

1._____

2._____

shatkam

1._____

2._____

sapthakam

1._____

2._____

ashtakam

1._____

2._____

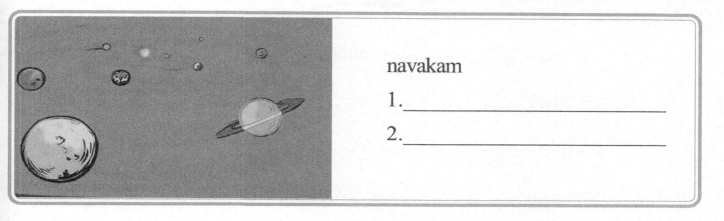

navakam

1._____

2._____

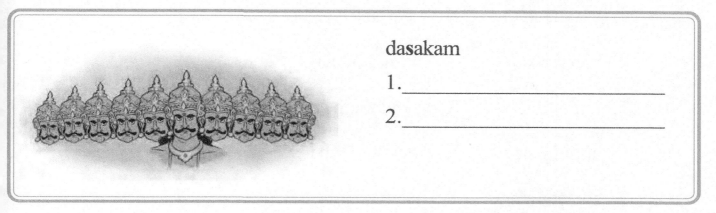

dasakam

1._____

2._____

Did you notice?

chathuhu + kam = chathurkam

chathuhu + kam = chathur+ kam= chathushkam ✓

III. Amarako:sam – Word Bank

1. Fire = pa:vakaha, havyava:hanaha , hutha:sanaha, ja:thave:da:ha, agnihi, a:sraya:saha

2. Ganges = Ganga:, Ja:nhavi:, Bha:gi:rathi:, Vishnupadi:, Thripatthaga:, Bhi:shmasu:hu

3. Ve:da = Ve:daha, A:mna:yaha, Sruthihi, Nigamaha, A:gamaha, Thrayi:

XIV. Learn Opposites

1. smruthaha   X   vismruthaha

2. ichchaya: X   anichchaya:

3. punya:ni   X   pa:pa:ni

4. a:ro:gyam   X   ana:ro:gyam

5. yasaha   X   ayasaha

6. baddhaha   X   vimukthaha

7. uktham   X   anuktham

8. adhi:thaha   X   anadhi:thaha

9. so:shanam   X   pla:vanam

10. vruddhihi   X   kshayaha

11. vya:dhihi   X   nirvya:dhihi

XV. Add prefixes or suffixes to make words. Make short sentences using the words.

Example: su+kham = sukham

		= sukham
		= duhkham

sukham   =   happiness

duhkham   =   sorrow

A. Join suffix 'yam' and construct words which mean 'it can be done' and make sentences if possible.

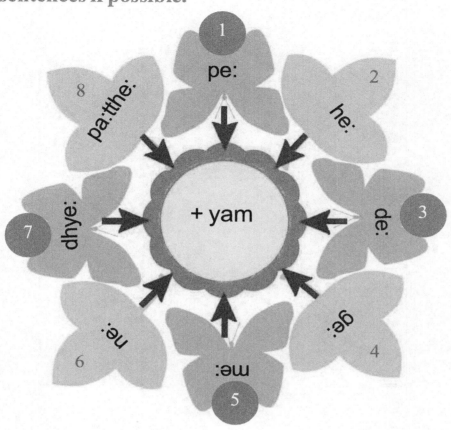

. <u>pe:yam</u> = which can be drunk   <u>apple juice pe:yam</u>

_____ = which can be given up   _____

. _____ = which can be given   _____

. _____ = which can be sung   _____

. _____ = which can be measured   _____

. _____ = which can be taken   _____

. _____ = which can be meditated   _____

. _____ = food which can be eaten in travel _____

B. Make words ending with 'i' called 'ika:ra:nthaha sabda' and mak
sentences if possible.

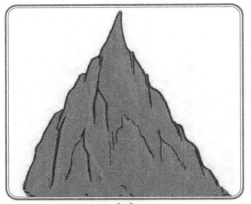
giri

+
hi

hari

kari

ari

sou:ri

1. <u>girihi</u>   = mountain.   <u>I climbed Thirumala girihi</u>

2. _____ = Lord Hari   _____

3. _____ = elephant   _____

4. _____ = enemy   _____

5. _____ = Lord Vishnu   _____

C. **Join suffix 'ya:m' and construct words in 7th case which mean 'in something' or 'on something' and make sentences if possible.**

1. <u>prutthivya:m</u>   = in the earth   <u>Prutthivya:m, we find diamonds</u>

2. _____ = in the river   _____

3. _____ = in sister   _____

4. _____ = in woman   _____

5. _____ = in the forest   _____

6. _____ = in the night   _____

D.   Here are some roots of verbs. Make sentences using the words if possible

1. <u>kri:danam</u>   = playing   <u>kri:danam is fun</u>

2. _____   = moving   _____

3. _____   = ruling/protecting_____

4. _____   = running   _____

5. _____   = burning   _____

6. _____   = drenching   _____

7. _____   = digging   _____

E. **Make compound words which mean 'bring something to you' and frame sentences if possible.**

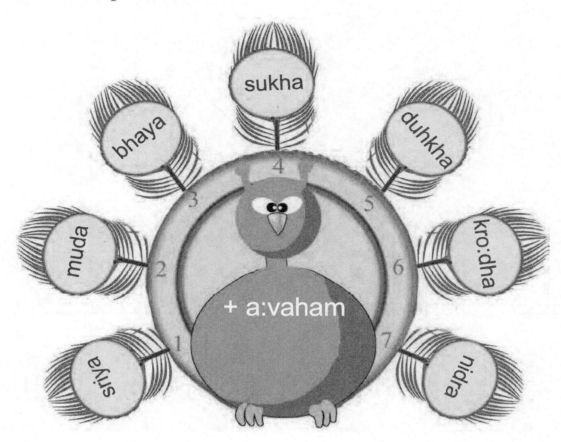

Ex - sriya+a:vaham = sriya:vaham

1. sriya:vaham   = which brings wealth   <u>Timely decision issriya:vaham</u>

2. _____ = which brings joy   _____

3. _____ = which brings fear   _____

4. _____ = which brings happiness   _____

5. _____ = which brings sorrow   _____

6. _____ = which brings anger   _____

7. _____ = which brings sleep

F. Make words ending with 'u' These words are called 'uka:ra:ntha sabda:s Frame sentences using them if possible.

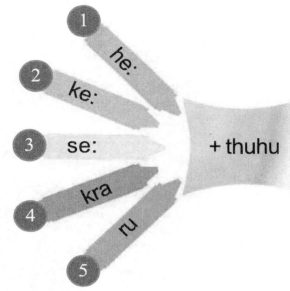

1. <u>he:thuhu</u>   = reason/cause   <u>Sunlight is he:thuhu in growing plants.</u>

2. _____   = planet ke:thu   _____

3. _____   = bridge   _____

4. _____   = ya:ga   _____

5. _____   = season   _____

G. Make compound words adding 'sa:raha' and make sentences if possible

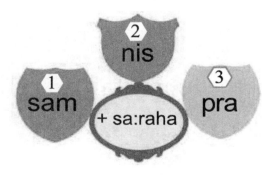

1. <u>samsa:raha</u>   = ego/ flow of ignorance <u>Creation is the result of samsa:raha</u>

2. _____   = dried   _____

3. _____   = broadcast   _____

H. Add suffix 'a:ya' to get words which mean 'after doing some activity' and make sentences if possible.

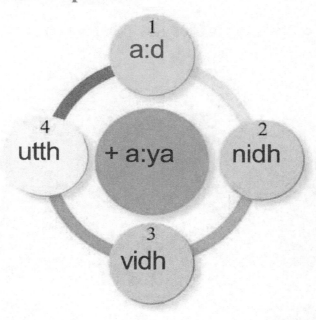

1. <u>a:daya</u>   = after taking   <u>Umbrella a:daya I went out in rain.</u>

2. _____ = after keeping   _____

3. _____ = after doing   _____

4. _____ = after awakening   _____

how the above activities through illustrations.

XVI. **Wonders with Prefixes.** In Sanskrit there are 22 prefixes by adding which
the meaning of the verb changes surprisingly…..

A. **Make words adding different prefixes to word 'harathi' and mak
sentences.**

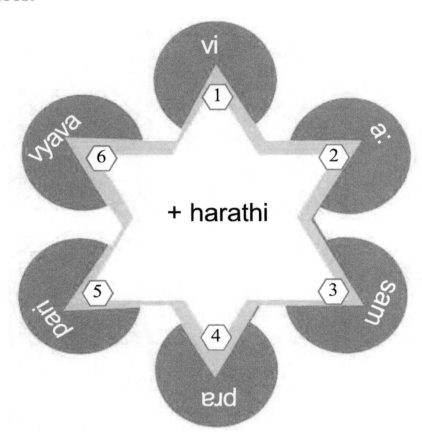

harathi = extinguishing

1. <u>viharathi</u>   = travelling with joy   <u>Krushna viharathi on the banks of Yamuna.</u>

2. _____   = bringing   _____

3. _____   = killing   _____

4. _____   = attacking   _____

5. _____   = solving/avoiding   _____

6. _____   = talking/administrating   _____

B. Make words adding different prefixes to word 'dhi:yathe:' and make sentences if possible.

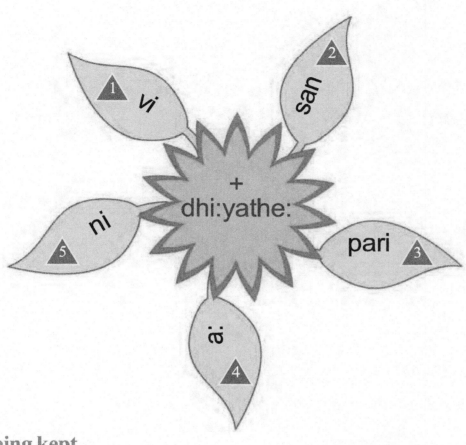

hi:yathe: = being kept

1. <u>vidhi:yathe:</u>   = being done / instructed   <u>Pu:ja vidhi:yathe: or To behave well</u>
<u>udent vidhi:yathe: .</u>

2. _____   = being attached   _____

3. _____   = being adorned   _____

4. _____   = being installed   _____

5. _____   = being offered   _____

C. Make words adding different prefixes to word 'ya:thi' and make sentence if possible.

ya:thi = going

1. <u>samya:thi</u>   =   pooling together   <u>Boy samya:thi all the coins.</u>

2. _____   =   losing   _____

3. _____   =   coming   _____

4. _____   =   going well   _____

XVII. Na:na:rtthas - means a word which has several different meanings.

Ex - Hari has several na:na:rtthas. See below.

Monkey

Lord Vishnu

Harihi

Lion

Frog

Horse

Sun

XVIII. Connect the Dots

XIX. Find 10 differences

XX. Picture Story - Keep the Rivers Clean.

 and went to by  . They went to take

bath in the  . While taking bath, they found that the was

and murky. The whole place was filled with bad  .

They saw a huge pile of as big as the  floating by.

The garbage was mainly ,  , dead  and

otten water  . They also found that the other  were

uffocating. The river 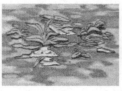 were dying. and felt .

They decided to educate everyone that is the source of life and we need to

rotect it.

Can you help them by writing 2 points on how to save our environment?

XXI. Label below places in the map

a) Gaya: b) River Ganga: c) Se:thu   d)Naimisa:ranyam

e) Pushkaram   f) Va:rana:si: g) Kurukshe:thra

Yajna is performed using sruk, sruvam, arani, samidha:s and pa:thra:s. Can you identify them in the picture below and color it.

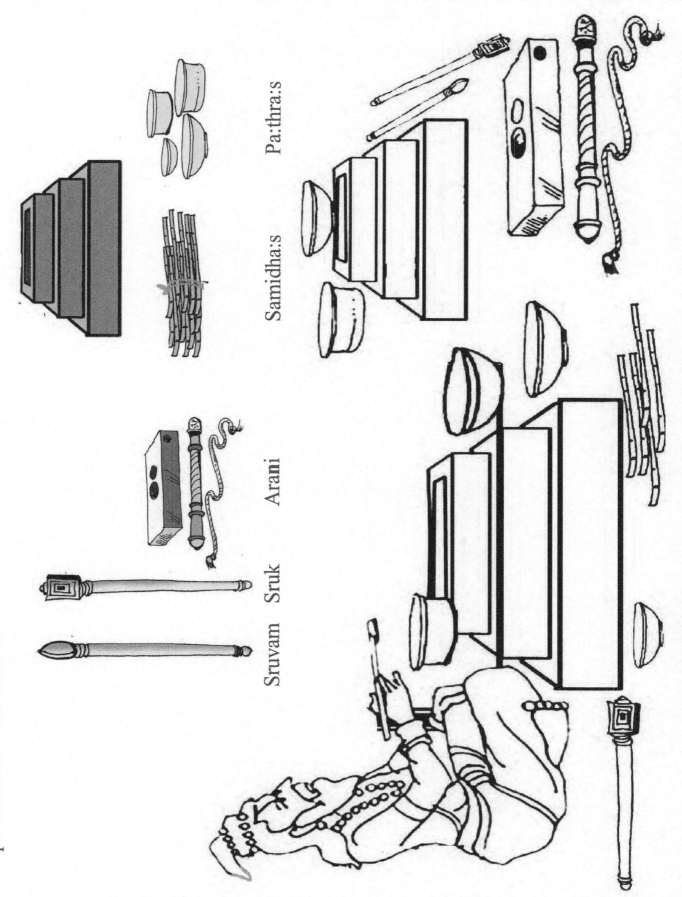

Sruvam   Sruk   Arani   Samidha:s   Pa:thra:s

XXIII. Draw

1. Va:nara:s constructing Ra:ma Se:thu over the ocean

2. Hari na:ma destroying all the sins

XXIV. Let us practice "da:nam"

'Da:nam' in Sanskrit means to donate. The Vedas instruct us to be charitable. It is our duty as a human being to perform charitable acts and extend a helping hand to the society around us.

Haryashtakam talks about go:da:nam and kanyada:nam. All the scriptures show us how to do charity. Lord Krishna preached in Bhagawad Gi:tha that one should do da:na:s and explained the details in 17th chapter.

Veda:s gave us directions on how to donate: *"sriya: de:yam hriya: de:yam bhiya: de:yam samvida de:yam"*

✿ sriya: de:yam   – donate according to your status

✿ hriya: de:yam   – donate with humility

✿ bhiya: de:yam   – whatever you donate, donate it with all its requirements, for example, if you donate a cow – donate a milk yielding cow along with its calf and fodder supply for one year

✿ samvida: de:yam – donate as recommended by scriptures and elders.

A. Below are some of the da:na:s mentioned in our scriptures. Color them.

1. go:da:nam - donate good milk yielding cows along with their calves

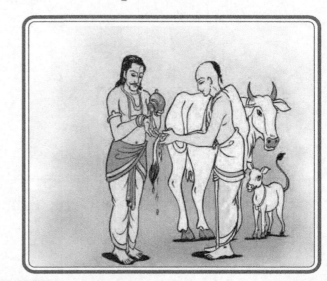

2. bhu:da:nam — donate good land

3.   vasthra da:nam — donate clothes

4.   anna da:nam — donate food

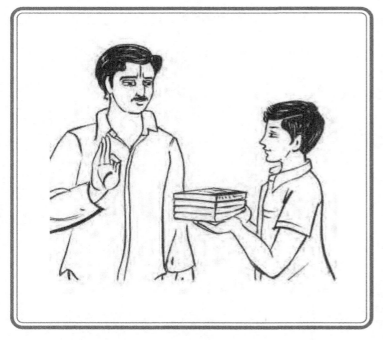

5.   vidya: da:nam –– Provide Education
      or donate books

6.   hiranya da:nam — donate gold

7. jala da:nam –- provide clean drinking water

8. sakthi da:nam – donate energy, time and service to community

9. anga da:nam

donate an organ

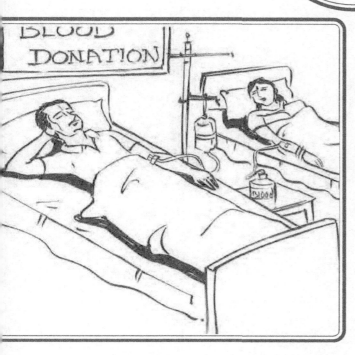

0. raktha da:nam – donate blood

11. ne:thra da:nam –- donate eyes

B. VT Seva (Volunteer Together for Service) volunteers are doing a food drive t donate food to Shelter homes. A group of volunteers went to the mall to reque them for donations. The grocery shop was kind enough and asked them to pic up few food items worth $1000 dollars. Can you help them identify the grocerie they need and put them in the shopping bags?

XXV. Do You Remember?

In Module 1, you learnt a slo:ka which is chanted while taking bath. It has names of a few sacred rivers.

a)   List the names of those rivers.

_____

b)   What is the name of the river mentioned in this stho:thra? What does it signify?

_____

XXVI. Research Activity

Collect the pictures of some popular bridges in the world. Name the bridges, locations and the materials with which they are made of? Compare their age with Nalase:thu constructed by Va:nara:s.

XXVII. Projects

1.   Construct a model bridge using popsicle sticks and see how much weight your bridge can hold?

2.   Construct a balance. Place 'Hari'na:ma written on a heavy metal badge and place it on one side of the balance. Write the names of all holy places, rivers, Ve:das on cotton balls and place them on other side of the balance. Display it showing everyone that Hari Na:ma overweighs all the holy places and activities.

XXVIII. Food for Thought

When do you remember the name of God intentionally and unintentionally?

1. A place or a river is holy because of its relationship with God.

2. This stho:thra was written by Prahla:da millions of years ago, so understand tha these places are NOT new, they are there since time immemorial sanctifying million of people for ages!

3. There are many things mentioned in this stho:thra that are **almost impossible** fc us to perform such as donating thousands of cows in charity, reciting all the Ve:das, performing Aswame:dha sacrifices, taking dip in all the holy rivers o Earth etc.

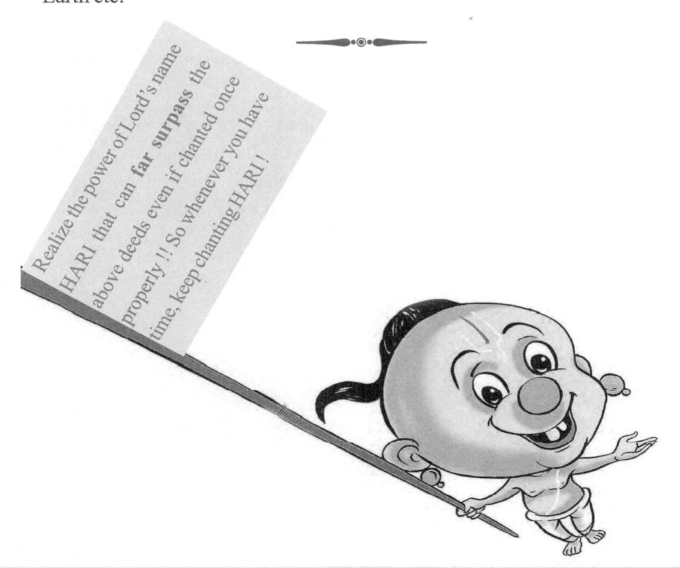

Realize the power of Lord's name HARI that can **far surpass** the above deeds even if chanted once properly !! So whenever you have time, keep chanting HARI !

Krushna:shtakam

krushnam vande jagadgurum

Krushna the naughtiest in the world but ever loved by everybody!

3. Krushna:shtakam

I. **Choose the correct answer**

1. Krushna is an incarnation of Lord
   a) Siva
   b) Bramha
   c) Na:ra:yana
   d) Indra

2. Krushna became "Jagad Guru" because
   a) he had thousands of students
   b) he drove the chariot
   c) he is God
   d) he spoke the universally applicable Bhagawad Gi:tha

3. Bhagawad Gi:tha means
   a) God's song
   b) God's play
   c) God's prose
   d) God's story

4. "kamsa cha:nura mardanaha" means one who
   a) is a friend of Kamsa and Cha:nura
   b) is a teacher of Kamsa and Cha:nu:ra
   c) killed the demons Kamsa and Cha:nu:ra
   d) both a and b

5. Krushna's eyes resemble
   a) those of a deer
   b) those of a fish
   c) wide open beautiful lotus petals
   d) none of the above

6. Ji:mu:tha means

    a) sky

    b) black bear

    c) cloud

    d) demon

7. Krushna's complexion is

    a) tan

    b) like that of a deep blue cloud

    c) gold

    d) milky white

8. _____ has a natural fragrance and is very much dear to Lord Krushna.

    a) Jasmine

    b) Rose

    c) Thulasi (Basil)

    d) All of the above

9. Vyjayanthi: is

    a) name of a go:pika

    b) a colorful garland

    c) Krushna's flute

    d) friend of Krushna

10. _____ represents Krushna's care for devotees.

    a) Sri:vathsa

    b) Vyjayanthi:

    c) Barhi pincha

    d) Parandha:ma

II. Fill in the blanks

1. _____ is the quintessence of Ve:das.

2. The whole universe is _____ divine body.

3. The eternal souls _____ and Muktha:s reside in divine abode called _____.

4. Kalpatharu is also called _____.

5. The mole on Krushna's chest is called _____.

6. The mole represents_____.

7. Chanting Krushna:shtakam removes ones' sins committed since _____ of births.

8. Krushna is decorated in _____ silk clothes.

9. Krushna was born with _____ hands.

10. Meditation means visualizing Krushna from _____ to _____

11. The guru of this universe is called _____.

12. Krushna's _____ is the abode for Sri: Lakshmi.

13. Krushna's birth place was a _____ .

14. Krushna was born in _____ dynasty.

15. Krushna's glittering wide eyes show His care and empathy for _____

III. Match Krushna's Relationships

1. Rukmini: a) devotees

2. Vasude:va   b) mother

3. Go:pika:s   c) father

4. De:vaki: d) uncle

5. Kamsa   e) wife

IV. **Complete the following words**

1. p___r___m___:n___nd___m

2. sut ____ a____

3. ba___hi

4. siro:r____ th____ ____ m

5. sri:ni___e:___ ham

V. **Fill in the slo:ka blanks**

1. neela _____ sannibham

2. _____maho:raskam vanama:la: vira:jitham

3. pu:rna _____ nibha:nanam

4. _____ gandha samyuktham

5. ava:ptha _____ gandham

6. _____ _____ dharam de:vam

7. Krushnam vande: _____

8. _____ ke:li samyuktham

VI. **Rearrange the words to reveal the slo:ka**

1. vande: 2. pi:tha:mbara   3. thulasi: 4. gandham

5. jagadgurum   6. rukmini: 7. krushnam 8. ke:li

9. samyuktham   10. ava:ptha   11 suso:bhitham

VII. Circle the odd man out

1. ha:ra, nu:pura, kankana, ke:yu:ram, kundala, chandra

2. padma pathra, thulasi:, kundala, athasi: pushpa

3. Kamsa, Cha:nu:ra, Ka:li:ya, Ra:vana, Pu:thana

4. nithya:s, muktha:s, Mushtika:sura, baddha:s

5. Rukmini:, De:vaki:, Yaso:da, Kausalya, Kaike:yi:

VIII. Analogy

1. De:vaki: is to Vasude:va as Kausalya: is to _____

2. Ra:ma is to Si:tha: as Krushna is to _____

3. Ha:ra is to neck as kankana is to _____

4. Krushna is to pi:tha:mbara as Vishwakse:na is to _____

5. Krushna's eyes is to lotus petal as Krushna's face is to _____

6. Nithya:s are to Paramapadam as human beings are to _____

7. Ve:das is to 4 as Purusha:rttha:s is to _____

8. Na:rada is to Vi:na as Krushna is to _____

9. Krushna is to compassion as cloud is to _____

10. Bhi:shma:charya is to Sri Vishnu Sahasrana:ma as _____ is to Bhagawad Gi:tha.

IX. One word answers

1. Who composed Krushna:shtakam?

   _____

2. Which tree fulfills all our wishes?

   _____

3. Who acts as a mediator between us and God?

   _____

4. What does 'cha:ru ha:sam' mean?

   _____

X. Answer the following

1. What do four hands of Krushna represent?

   _____

   _____

2. List the various ornaments that Krushna wore.

   _____

   _____

3. Explain why Lord is decorated with lots of beautiful jewellery?

   _____

   _____

4. What does Krushna's deep blue glow signify?

_____

_____

5. What should one do to become the best amongst all?

_____

_____

6. What does **Sri**:vathsa signify?

_____

_____

7. What are the benefits of chanting Krushna:shtakam?

_____

_____

XI. Complete the patterns by choosing the correct answer from pink boxes.

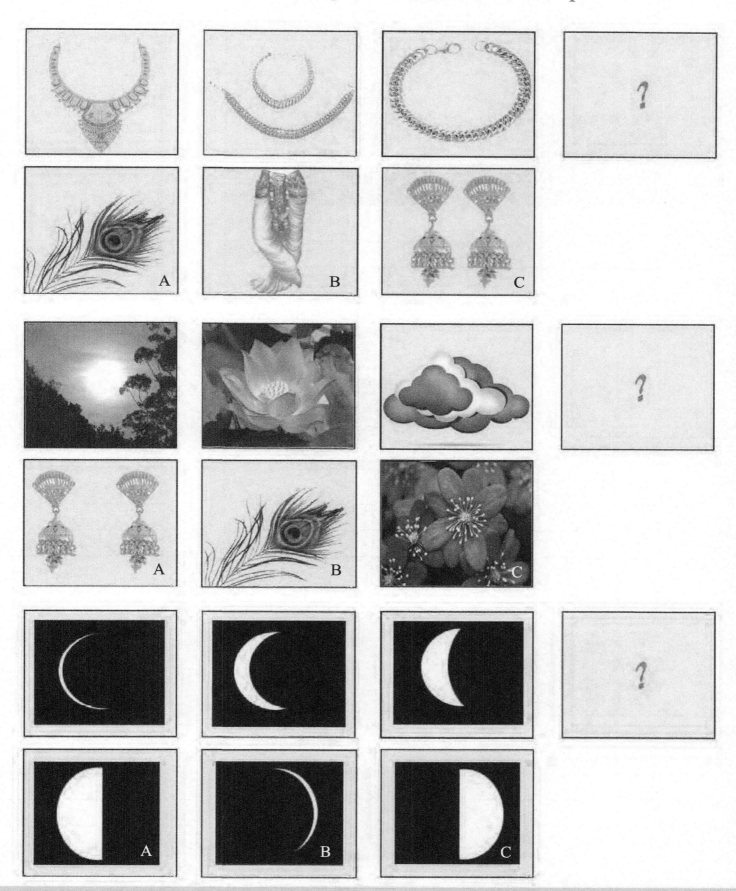

XII. **Almost every slo:ka compares Lord Krushna's appearance or qualities wit**
     Nature. Number the jumbled pictures as per the order of slo:kas, label ther
     and write the first word of the slo:ka

_____	_____	_____
_____	_____	_____
_____	_____	_____

_____	_____	_____
_____	_____	_____
_____	_____	_____

_____	_____
_____	_____
_____	_____

III. Amarako:sam – Word Bank

1. lotus   = padmam, nalinam, aravindam, kamalam, panke:ruham, sarasi:ruham, sa:rasam, tha:marasam

2. face   = a:nanam, vakthram, vadanam, mukham, lapanam, thundam, a:syam

3. son   = suthaha, a:thmajaha, thanayaha, puthraha, su:nuhu

4. cloud   = ji:mu:thaha, abhram, me:ghaha, va:riva:haha, jaladharaha, va:ridaha, mudiraha, jalamuk

IV. Na:na:rttha:s

Do you know that there are multiple meanings for the word "Krushna"?

waning moon

black color

Lord Krushna

black pepper

XV. Opposites

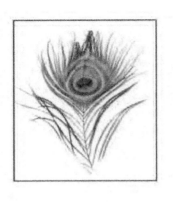   e:kam   X   ane:kam

   uttha:ya   X   upavisya

   de:vaha   X   ra:kshasaha

duhkham   X   sukham

 punyam X pa:pam

 uthphulla padmam X mukulitha padmam

 ni:la ji:mu:tham X swe:tha:mbaram

 ava:ptha gandham X nirgatha gandham

XVI.   A. Join the prefix 'sam' to make words and make sentences if possible.

Ex - sam + bhavaha = sambhavaha

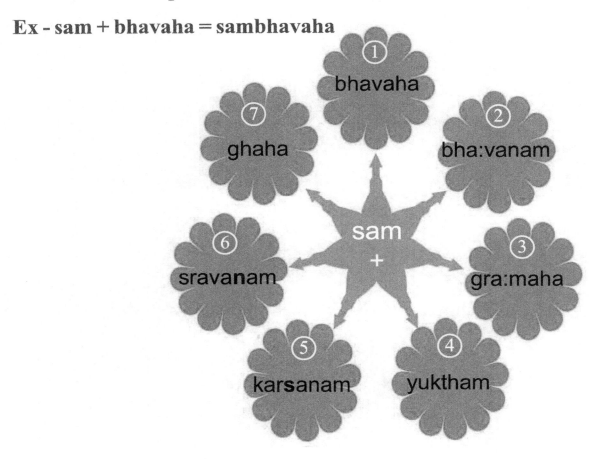

1. <u>sambhavaha</u>   = possibility   <u>It is too hot. There is sambhavaha to rai</u>

2. _____   = honorarium   _____

3. _____   = war   _____

4. _____   = attached   _____

5. _____   = tilling/pulling   _____

6. _____   = keen listening   _____

7. _____   = society   _____

B. Join the suffix 'daha' to make words and make sentences if possible.

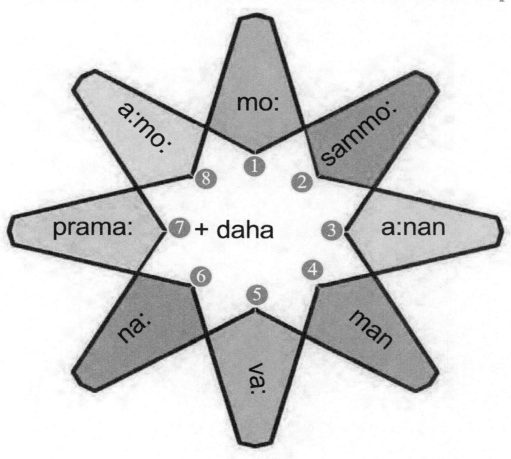

1. <u>mo:daha</u>   = happiness   <u>By learning slo:kas, I get mo:daha.</u>

2. _____   = joy   _____

3. _____   = bliss   _____

4. _____   = lazy person   _____

5. _____   = debate   _____

6. _____   = music   _____

7. _____   = not alert   _____

8. _____   = fragrance/acceptance _____

C. **Make compound words to get the masters of various things and fram
sentences if possible.**

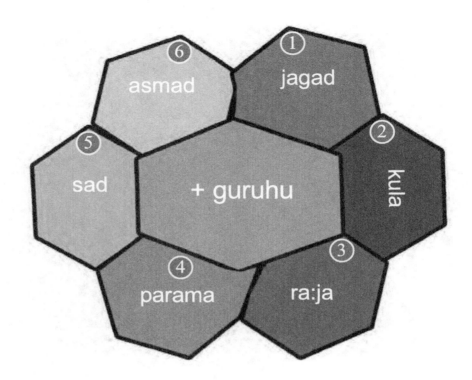

1. <u>jagadguruhu</u>   = mentor of the Universe   <u>Krushna is jagadguruhu</u>

2. _____   = mentor of the clan   _____

3. _____   = king among the guru:s   _____

4. _____   = guru of all the guru:s   _____

5. _____   = spiritual master   _____

6. _____   = our mentor   _____

D. **Join suffix 'ane:na' and construct words in 3rd case which tell about some activity and form sentences if possible.**

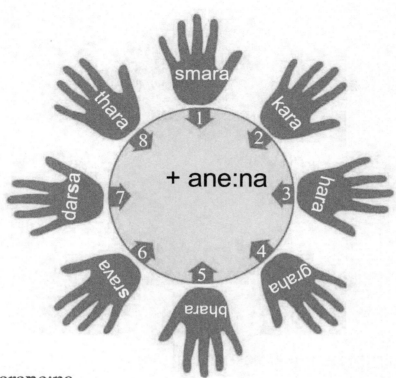

smara + ane:na = smarane:na

1. <u>smarane:na</u>   = by remembering   <u>I gain courage harina:ma smarane:na.</u>

2. _____   = by instrument   _____

3. _____   = by vanishing   _____

4. _____   = by taking   _____

5. _____   = by holding/ bearing   _____

6. _____   = by listening   _____

7. _____   = by looking   _____

8. _____   = by crossing   _____

E. Join these words to make compound words to get the best among the grou and form sentences if possible.

ya:dava:na:m

de:va:na:m

cha:thra:na:m

+ siro:rathnam

ba:la:na:m

ji:va:na:m

go:pika:na:m

1   2   6   3   5   4

☞ **These words are using 6th case**

1. <u>ya:dava:na:m siro:rathnam</u>= best one among all ya:dava:s.

   <u>Krushna is Ya:dava:na:m siro:rathnam</u>

2. _____ = best one among all de:vatha:s.

   _____

3. _____ = best among all kids

   _____

4. _____ = best among all go:pika:s

   _____

5. _____ = best among all beings

   _____

6. _____ = best among all students

   _____

F. Join these words to make compound words to get beautiful things and form sentences if possible.

 These words are using 2nd case

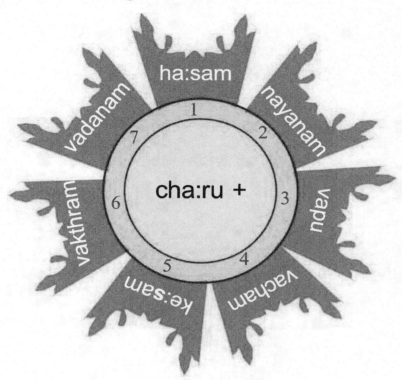

1. <u>cha:ru+ha:sam</u>= beautiful smile   <u>Krushna has cha:ruha:sam</u>

2. _____ = beautiful eye   _____

3. _____ = beautiful skin   _____

4. _____ = beautiful talk   _____

5. _____ = beautiful hair   _____

6. _____ = beautiful face   _____

7. _____ = beautiful face   _____

G. Join these words and make atleast 5 phrases.

Ex. vilasath makuta dharam

	kundala	
vilasath	makuta	
lasath	kankana	dharam
	ha:ra	
	ke:yu:ra	
	nu:pura	

H. Join suffix 'na:m' and construct words and form sentences if possible.

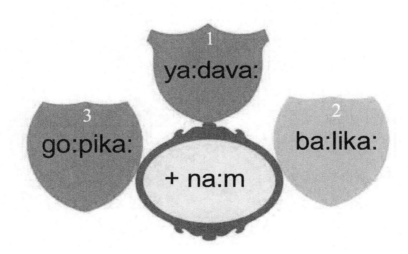

1. <u>go:pika:na:m</u> = of Go:pika:s'   <u>Go:pika:na:m dance is beautiful.</u>

2. _____ = of Ya:dava:s'   _____

3. _____ = of Girls'   _____

I. Join these words to make compound words and form sentences if possible.

1. <u>cha:**nu**:ra mardanam=pounding Cha:**nu**:ra I bow to God who is Cha:**nu**:ra</u>

    <u>mardanam.</u>

2. _____ = pounding Ka:**li**:ya _____

3. _____ = pounding Mura _____

4. _____ = pounding Kamsa _____

5. _____ = pounding Mahisha _____

6. _____ = pounding enemy _____

7. _____ = massaging oil _____

8. _____ = mixing dough

J. **Join these words to make compound words and write the meaning.**

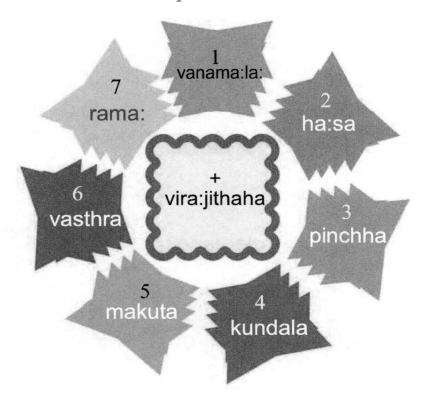

1.

_____

2.

_____

3.

_____

4.

_____

5.

_____

6.

_____

7.

_____

K. Join these words and make atleast 5 phrases.

Krushnaha		thulasi: gandhaha
Aham (I)		pusthakaha
Thwam (You)	ava:ptha (who has)	mano:ratthaha
E:shaha (This person)		udyo:gaha
Saha (That person)		vasthraha
ba:laha (kid)		jna:naha

XVII. Learn more - Flower is called 'pushpam' in sanskrit.

kamalam = lotus

pa:tala = rose

mallika: = jasmine

champakam = champa

athasi: = flax

su:ryamukham = sun flower

XVIII. Find atleast 10 differences

XIX. Color

I am doing pu:ja to Sri Krushna using tho:yam, phalam, pushpam, pathram, di:pam, dhu:pam, ha:rathi, cha:maram, ma:la:, tha:mbu:lam. Can you identify them and color the picture above.

XX. What is wrong in the picture?

83

XXI. Picture puzzle. Can you spot 11 Lord Kṛṣṇas in this picture?

XXII. Label each part of Krushna's beauty with the phrases given in th
Krushna:shtakam as shown in the example

kutila:laka samyuktham

XXIII. Let us practice

A) Protect and Cherish Nature and its Beauty

a) Nature is beautiful. A majestic lion, a colorful rainbow, beautiful peacock feathers, gorgeous sun rise and sun set, the deep blue oceans, snowcapped mountains, trees laden with colorful and sweet smelling flowers and fruits, the fragrant flowers fill our hearts with joy. Beauty in anything comes from Lord Krushna. Lord Krushna is the personification of beauty. Let us all enjoy Sri Krushna's beauty by enjoying the beauty of Nature.

Let us enjoy and nourish Nature

Let us live with Nature

Let us not destroy Nature

Let us use products of Nature

Let us refrain from using products which destroy Nature

Let us own Nature

Let us protect Nature

Let us nurture Nature

Let us enjoy Krushna's presence in every part of Nature

b) What products can be replaced with eco-friendly products? Can you list more than two items?

c) The Go:vardhana Mountain is filled up with garbage. A few VT Seva (Volunteer Together for Service) volunteers are volunteering as part of 4 Rs project (REDUCE, REUSE, RECYCLE and REPAIR) to clean up the place. Can you help them identify different categories of trash and place it in the appropriate bins?

B. Let us practice: Sousi:lyam

The virtue of great people befriending people lower in status without inhibition is called 'sousi:lyam'. Lord Krushna is the lord of the Universe. He is the master of all souls. Yet out of compassion, He took birth as a human being and grew up in Nandavraj amongst the uneducated cowherd boys and girls, taking care of the cattle.

Let us all develop this quality. Let us not become arrogant because of our knowledge, wealth, status in society, or family background. Let us treat everyone with respect and lend a helping hand to the underprivileged.

VT Seva volunteers are doing service activity for the poor blind students in VT Seva School and College for the Blind.

Can you suggest what you would like to do for them?

1. _____

2. _____

XXIV. Do You Remember?

In Module 1, you learnt the below slo:ka glorifying the beauty of Lor
Krushna. Complete the blanks.

kasthu:ri: thilakam _____ _____

_____,

vakshas**tth**ale: _____,na:sa:gre:

_____,

karathale: _____ kare:

_____,

sarva:nge: _____ kalayan, kan**tt**e: cha

_____,

go:pasthri: _____ vijayathe: ,

_____ chu:da:manihi

XXV. Research Activity

1. I don't want to commit this_____ because it is a sin. What ar
   they?

   _____

2. List the benefits of Thulasi plant.

   _____

   _____

3. Name a few devotees of Lord Krushna.

   _____

   _____

XXVI. Do you know?

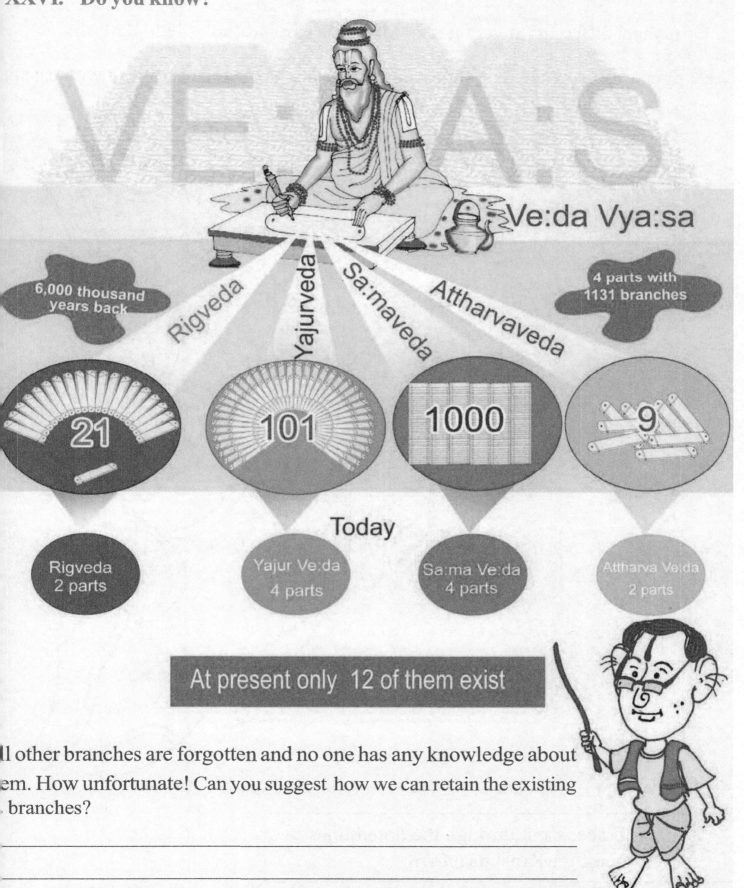

Ve:da Vya:sa

6,000 thousand years back

Rigveda

Yajurveda

Sa:maveda

Attharvaveda

4 parts with 1131 branches

21

101

1000

9

Today

Rigveda 2 parts

Yajur Ve:da 4 parts

Sa:ma Ve:da 4 parts

Attharva Ve:da 2 parts

At present only 12 of them exist

ll other branches are forgotten and no one has any knowledge about
em. How unfortunate! Can you suggest how we can retain the existing
branches?

_____

_____

XXVII. Projects

1. Collect different flowers and try to make a garland and offer to Krushna.

2. Prepare a crown for Krushna using gold color paper and decorate it with peacoc
    feathers.

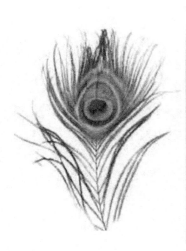

 Trace & cut through the doted lines to
make the Krushna crown

XXVIII. Food for thought

Who doesn't want to be beautiful? Everyone.

We want to look beautiful. We want our surroundings to look beautiful too. Physical beauty can be acquired from Nature. We can also see and enjoy that beauty in Nature.

To make our mind beautiful, we should learn to feel the presence of Krushna in everything and decorate our mind with His beauty. All the jewellery, fruits, flowers describing Krushna are from Nature. Nature is used to describe Krushna's beauty because Nature is beautiful. See Krushna in your mind and experience the inner and outer beauty. Then the experience becomes holistic.

But why should we think only of Krushna?

It is because children like games. They like to play, sing, dance and enjoy. Krushna did all these activities in his childhood. He was very mischievous but at the same time, all his acts were filled with divinity. Thus, he captured the hearts of children and elders.

Hence, whoever wants to be beautiful, hook on to Krushna.

Pancha:yudha Stho:thram

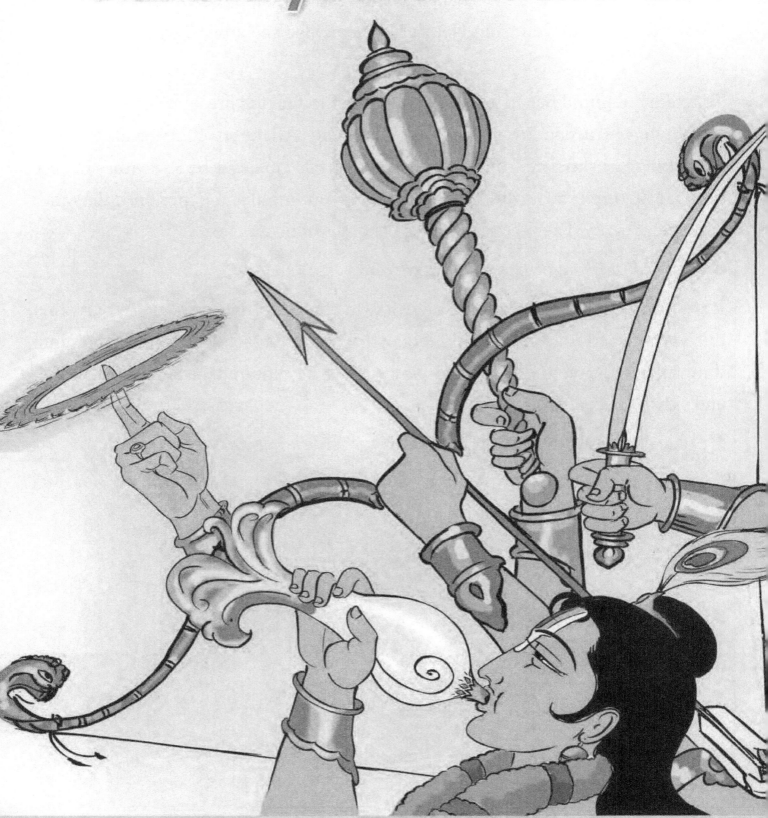

4. Pancha:yudha Stho:thram

I. Choose the correct answer

1. _____ is lustrous white.
   a) Sudarsana
   b) Pa:nchajanya
   c) Sa:rngam
   d) Kaumo:daki:

2. _____ enables us to see the divine form of Lord.
   a) Pa:nchajanya
   b) Sudarsana
   c) Kaumo:daki:
   d) Sa:rngam

3. 'Sphurath' means
   a) killing
   b) protecting
   c) radiating
   d) none of the above

4. _____are compared to scorching sunlight and cool moonlight respectively.
   a) Sudarsana and Kaumo:daki:
   b) Sudarsana and Pa:nchajanya
   c) Sarngam and Pa:nchajanya
   d) Kaumo:daki: and Nandakam

5. This weapon is made of gold
   a) Sudarsana
   b) Pa:nchajanya
   c) Sa:rngam
   d) Kaumo:daki:

6. Pancha:yudha Stho:thra when chanted every morning eradicates

    a) all darkness

    b) all sins and miseries

    c) all diseases

    d) all of the above

7. 'che:tha:msi' means

    a) people

    b) demons

    c) hearts

    d) de:vatha:s

8. Lord wears a great gem called

    a) Sri:vathsa

    b) Kousthubham

    c) Vyjayanthi

    d) Pa:rija:tha

9. 'Sadyaha' means

    a) always

    b) never

    c) sometimes

    d) instantly

10. Lord holds _____ with lower left hand.

    a) Sudarsana

    b) Pa:nchajanya

    c) Sa:rngam

    d) Kaumo:daki:

II. Fill in the blanks

1. Sudarsana means _____.

2. God holds weapons for the sake of_____.

3. Lord Vishnu holds _____ weapons.

4. Chanting Pancha:yudha Stho:thra regularly strengthens one's _____and _____ in God.

5. _____become instantly fearless upon hearing the sounds echoed from _____ strings.

III. Match the following

1.	Vara:ha	a.	Water
2.	Ke:sava	b.	Land
3.	Narasimha	c.	Forest
4.	Va:mana	d.	At all times
5.	Sudarsana	e.	Sword
6.	Pa:nchajanya	f.	Conch
7.	Kaumo:daki:	g.	Gem
8.	Nandakam	h.	Mole
9.	Sa:rngam	i.	Bow
10.	Sri:vathsa	j.	Disc
11.	Kausthubham	k.	Mace

IV. True or false

1. Man has no difficulties.

2. Man is independent from Nature.

3. Animals do not become victims of their own arrogance.

4. Meditating on the five weapons enhances our faith multifold.

5. God needs lots of weapons and jewels.

V. Complete the following words

1. srava___ ___:___h

2. bh___y___:n___

3. su___ ___a:n___

4. d___r___a

5. p___ ___ ch___

VI. Fill in the slo:ka blanks

1. che:tha:msi ——————— ——————— sadyaha

2. sudarsanam ——————— ——————— thulyam

3. yasya dhvanir ——————— ———————— hantha:

4. ———————— daithya kulaika hanthri:m

5. _____sada:ham saranam prapadye:

VII. Rearrange the words to reveal the slo:ka

1. va:ra:haha	2. va:manaha	3. rakshathu	4. na:rasimhaha
5. sarvathah	6. pa:thu	7. jale:	8. stthale:
9. rakshathu	10. atavya:m	11. ke:savaha	12. cha

VIII. Circle the odd man out

1. meditation, prayer, courage, chanting, worship

2. east, south, west, north, up, down, middle

3. sea, pool, forest, ocean, lake, river

4. da:nava, daithya, asura, sura

5. pi:tha:mbaram, kausthubham, ni:la:mbaram, sri:vathsam, sri:

6. Va:mana, Narasimha, Vara:ha, Ke:sava, Parasura:ma.

IX. Analogy

1. Sudarsana is to scorching sun as pa:nchajanya is to _____.

2. Kaumo:daki: is to Mount Me:ru as Sa:rngam is to _____.

3. Krushna is to Sudarsana as Rama is to _____.

4. Pa:nchajanya is to O:M as _____ is to vision of Lord.

5. Mace is to Kaumo:daki: as sword is to _____.

6. Pa:nchajanya is to left hand as Sudarsana is to _____.

7. Jala is to water as agni is to _____

8. Arjuna's conch is to De:vadaththa as Krushna's conch is to _____.

9. Weapons is to protection as ornaments is to _____.

10. _____ is to Krushna as swe:tha:mbaram is to Vishwakse:na.

X. Short Answers

1. Which avatha:ra protects us from risks in water?

   _____

2. Which avatha:ra protects us from calamities on land?

   _____

3. Which avatha:ra protects us from dangers in woods?

   _____

4. Which avatha:ra protects us always?

   _____

5. What makes man to become brave or fearful?

   _____

6. What weapon is described to have Lord's breath as its food?

   _____

7. Which weapon makes thunderous sounds?

   _____

8. What does 'darpa' mean?

   _____

9. Whom do we pray to in Pancha:yudha stho:thram?

   _____

10. What puts our thoughts in right direction?

    _____

XI. **Answer the following**

    1.   Does God need any weapons or jewelry? Describe.

    _____

    _____

    2.   Can man control Nature? Elaborate.

    _____

    _____

    3.   Is man independent? Explain.

    _____

    _____

    4.   Who can mould our thought process?

    _____

    _____

XII. **Complete the patterns by choosing the correct answer from pink boxes.**

2.

3.

4.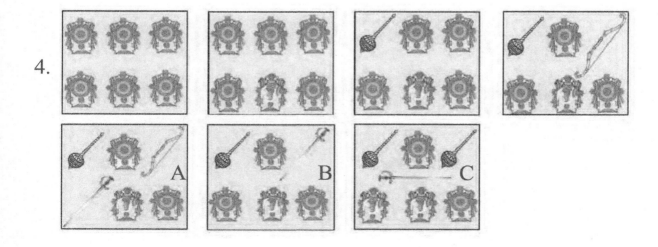

XIII. Number the jumbled pictures as per the order of slo:ka:s, label them and write the first word of the slo:ka

_____

_____

_____

_____

_____

_____

_____

_____

_____

_____

_____

_____

_____

XIV. Can you help Ravi sort and put the bags in appropriate carts?

Help, greed, perfection, Vishnu, selfish, lies, fire accident, rude, Va:mana, Mathsya, integrity, Narasimha, earthquake, Vara:ha, Ke:sava, theft, honesty, ego, arrogance, fear, famine, radiation, kindness, trust, disrespect, Krushna, Balara:ma, Parasura:ma, pride, cunning, hurt, slapping, respect, service, accidents, unemployment, poverty, unrest, avalanche, duplicity, wickedness

XV. Learn the Words. These words are using 7th case.

vane:	= in the forest	gagane:	= in the sky
rane:	= in the war	madhye:	= in the middle
jale:	= in the water	anthe:	= at the end
stthale:	= on the land	pra:rambhe:	= in the beginning

XVI. Amarako:sam – Word Bank

de:vaha =   suraha, amaraha, nirjaraha, thridasaha, a:dithe:yaha, vibudhaha, amarthyaha, adithinandanaha

sun   =   bha:skaraha, su:ryaha, diva:karaha, ahaskaraha, prabha:karaha, a:dithyaha

cloth   =   ambaraha, vasthram, vasanam, va:saha, a:chcha:danam, amsukam, che:laha

moon   =   himamsuhu, chandraha, induhu, kumudaba:ndhavaha, sasadharaha, nisa:mpathihi, so:maha, glauhu, kala:nidhihi, nakshathre:saha, mruga:nkaha, o:shadhi:saha

vishnuhu   = na:rayanaha, krushnaha, vaikunttaha, vishtarasrava:ha, da:mo:daraha, hrushi:ke:saha

XVII. Na:na:rttha:s - Do you know the different meanings of the word Saranam?

Saranam =   Home, protector, surrenderance

XVIII. Opposite Words

1. rakshanam   X   dandanam
2. mithram   X   satruhu
3. suraha   X   asuraha
4. madhye: X   parithaha
5. bhaya:ni   X   abhaya:ni
6. sadyaha   X   vilambe:na
7. a:kula:thma: X   ana:kula:thma:
8. prabha:the: X   ra:thrau
9. yadruchchaya: X   swe:chchaya:
10. va:makaraha   X   dakshinakaraha

XIX. A. Join syllables to get different time periods and make sentences i possible.

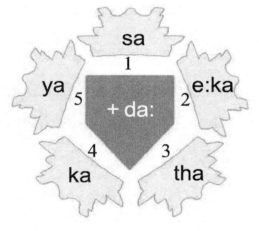

1. _____ = always   _____

2. _____ = once   _____

3. _____ = then   _____

4. _____ = when   _____

5. _____ = whenever   _____

B. **Join the words with prefix "su" to make words.**

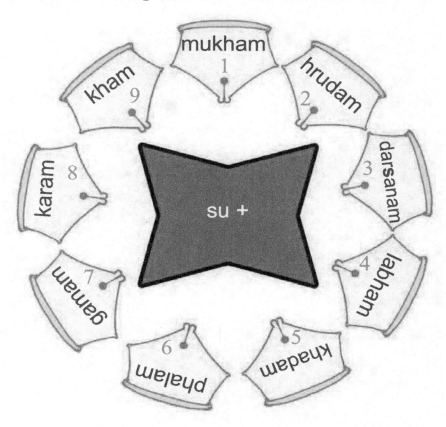

x. su+prathishttitham = suprathishttitham means - well established

1. _____ = pleasant

2. _____ = good hearted

3. _____ = beautiful/good looks

4. _____ = good result

5. _____ = easy to acquire

6. _____ = which gives happiness

7. _____ = easy to reach

8. _____ = easy to do

9. _____ = ease/happy

C. Join suffix 'nam' to make words and form sentences if possible.

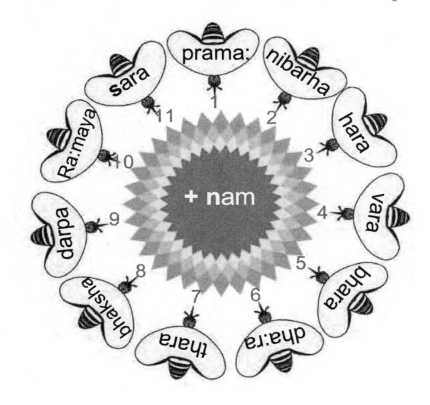

1. _____ = authentic   Ve:da is unquestionably prama:**n**am.

2. _____ = destroy   _____

3. _____ = to steal   _____

4. _____ = to choose   _____

5. _____ = to hear   _____

6. _____ = to wear   _____

7. _____ = to cross   _____

8. _____ = to eat/eatable   _____

9. _____ = mirror   _____

10. _____ = abode of Ra:ma   _____

11. _____ = home/protector/mode_____

D.   Join suffix 'kshaha' to make words and make sentences if possible.

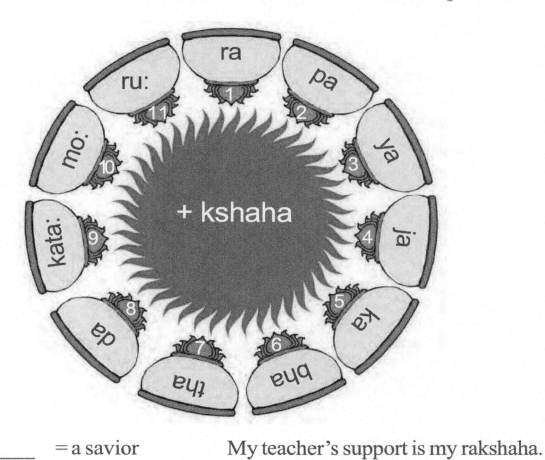

1.   _____ = a savior   My teacher's support is my rakshaha.

2.   _____ = a part/wing   _____

3.   _____ = Kube:ra   _____

4.   _____ = an eater   _____

5.   _____ = a bush   _____

6.   _____ = an eater   _____

7.   _____ = a carpenter   _____

8.   _____ = a skillful   _____

9.   _____ = a vision   _____

10. _____ = release   _____

11. _____ = an unpallatable   _____

E. **Join words to make compound words, write the meanings and make sentence
if possible.**

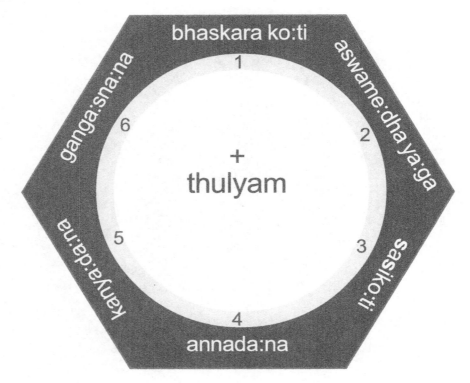

1. _____

2. _____

3. _____

4. Chanting hari na:ma is anna da:na thulyam.

5. _____

6. _____

F. Join words to get different types of wheels, write meanings and form sentences if possible.

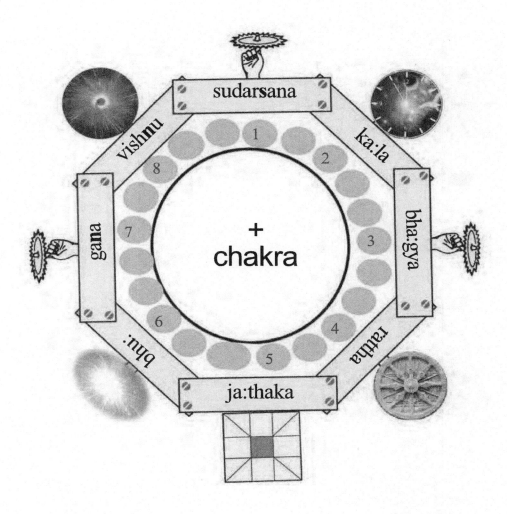

1. _____

2. _____

3. _____

4. _____

5. _____

6. _____

XX. **Color the Sankha, Chakra, Thiruna:mam and decorate the faces of kids wit** Na:mam.

XXI. Connect the dots and label the pictures.

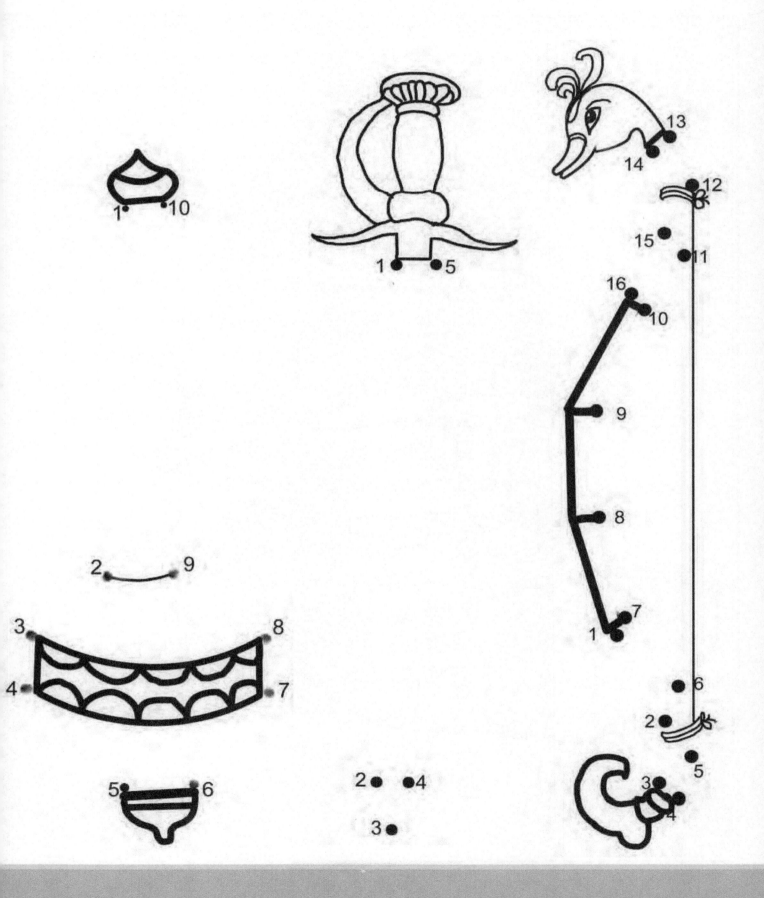

XXII.   Find at least 10 sankha:s and 10 chakra:s in the picture below.

XXIII.   What is wrong in the picture below?

XXIV. Find 10 Differences

XXV. Picture Story

Eka:dasi vratham is an austerity where one fasts, sings names of Lord and skips that night's sleep. Dwa:dasi vratham is another austerity where one chants the names of Lord and eats prasadam in the early hours. Ambari:sha was a great devotee of Lord Hari. On every Eka:dasi day,  used to perform Eka:dasi vratham and conclude on the following Dwa:dasi day by doing Dwa:dasi vratha. On Dwa:dasi, he used to offer prayers to , invite Vedic scholars , honor them with new , and other .

He used to offer feast to all guests before breaking his fast. On one such Dwa:dasi day, Durvasa:, arrived at the . invited to accept his hospitality. agreed. Sage wanted to finish his afternoon rituals in the . He asked to wait until he returned.

The auspicious time to break the fast was fast approaching. To test the commitmen

of , did not return intentionally. Taking the advice of  Vasishta

 drank a little  with  leaf and broke his fast. Then returne

 . felt insulted for broke his fast before honoring the guest. In

fit of rage, he created a  from a strand of his  to kill

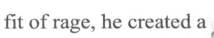

However, Lord's Sudarsana  killed the  and proceeded to attac

 . went to  and  for protection but bot

expressed their inability to save  .

, out of fear approached also. said," is a great

votee. Ask him to forgive you for your arrogance!" finally approached

 and sought for forgiveness. A real devotee is always humble. Hence,

It embarrassed and prayed to  and thus saved .

Moral of the story

* Don't hurt devotees. God cannot tolerate that.

* Always fast on Eka:dasi. Eat in early hours on Dwa:dasi.

* God and His weapons always protect his devotees.

* God respects His devotees more than Himself.

* Sudarsana stands first in protecting Lord's devotees.

* Your unshakable faith in God will always protect you.

Interesting Fact - In Thirumala, the weapons of Lord Venkate:swara are worshipped first before offering services to the Lord.

XXVI. Let us Practice- Use objects appropriately

God is everywhere. He is present in each and every atom of this Univers
Experiencing His divine presence in any place or object makes that place
object holy. Thus, even the tools become divine and reverential. Invoke th
power of God with faith, and use the tools for right purposes. Do not abuse th
tools by using them for immoral purposes.

VT Seva volunteering kids are conducting a garage sale to raise funds for educating the Tribal kids in India. There are different tools on sale. Can you identify them and classify how they are used by a good person and a bad person.

repare a chart to show how the following tools are used by a good person and a
ad person.

TOOLS	BAD	GOOD

XXVII. Do You Remember?

a) Which slo:ka from Pancha:yudha stho:thram is chanted before travelling? You already learned this in Module 1. _____

b) Below is another slo:ka you learned in Module 1. Rearrange the words to frame that slo:ka.

1. aham
2. sri:ra:mam
3. sampada:m
4. apahartha:ram
5. a:pada:m
6. nama:mi
7. lo:ka:bhira:mam
8. da:tha:ram
9. bhu:yaha
10. bhu:yaha
11. sarva

c) Whom are you praying to in the above slo:ka? Why should we pray to God before travelling?

XXVIII. Research Activity

1. What weapons were used in olden days?

2. Find the stho:thram that has 1000 names of Lord Vishnu.

3. Who procured independence to India using non-violence as his weapon?

4. Name the incarnations and weapons used in those incarnations by Lord Sri: Har

XXIX. Project

1. Prepare a bow and arrow using sticks and thread.

2. Can you prepare a mace using base ball bat, a big ball and color paper?

3. Can you name two personalities from our scriptures who used the above weapons?

XXX. Food for thought

Which ornament/weapon do you consider most beautiful for you whe Lord holds it?

Weapons and ornaments are both attractive to devotees and fearful to wicked people.

Gaje:ndra Mo:kshanam

5. Gaje:ndra Mo:kshanam

I. **Choose the correct answer**

1. The root cause of whole universe is
   a) Bramha
   b) Rudra
   c) Indra
   d) Lord Na:ra:yana

2. 'Mo:kshanam' means
   a) getting caught
   b) getting released
   c) getting protection
   d) getting salvation

3. 'Mo:ksham' means
   a) getting salvation
   b) getting released
   c) getting protection
   d) getting caught

4. 'gra:ha grasthe:' means being
   a) protected by Lord
   b) caught by a crocodile
   c) released by Lord
   d) blessed by Lord

5. Lord Sri:manna:rayana is the ultimate protector and savior of all
   a) plants and animals
   b) human beings
   c) insects and amphibians
   d) all of the above

6. When Lord was not satisfied with the speed of Garuda,

    a) he left Garuda

    b) he asked Garuda to go faster

    c) he added His own speed to Garuda and went even faster

    d) he took another vehicle

7. Ultimately, Gaje:ndra prayed " _____ "

    a) Oh Bramha! please come and protect me

    b) Oh Indra! please come and protect me

    c) Let that originator and the root cause of this entire Universe come and protect me

    d) Oh Siva! come and protect me

8. 'Abhaya' mudra by Lord denotes His _____ to devotees.

    a) assurance of protection

    b) supremacy

    c) power

    d) none of the above

9. Initially Gaje:ndra

    a) was jealous of other elephants

    b) was proud of his valor

    c) was a lazy elephant

    d) was very humble

10. As Gaje:ndra Mo:kshanam has 2 slo:ka:s, it is also called

    a) Slo:ka dvayam

    b) Slo:ka dvikam

    c) Gaje:ndra dvayam

    d) a & b only

II. Fill in the blanks

1. Gaje:ndra had knowledge of its previous _____.

2. Gaje:ndra was bathing on Mount _____.

3. Gaje:ndra was caught by an _____.

4. Lord Sri:manna:ra:yana appeared as _____ to save Gaje:ndra.

5. Gaje:ndra Mo:kshanam proves that _____alone is th
sole_____ of all souls.

III. Match the following

1. tha:rkshyaha   a. garuda
2. mu:la ka:ranam   b. origin and root cause of Universe
3. nakra   c. sign of protection
4. abhaya   d. prosperity
5. mangalam   e. crocodile

IV. Unscramble the words

1. HANA   _____

2. MARAS   _____

3. MISA   _____

4. USAA   _____

5. THAY   _____

V. Fill in the slo:ka blanks

1. _____ _____ kari:ndre: _____nayane:

2. hasthaih_____ apyavathu hari rasau

3. a:bibhra:no: _____abhayam

4. na:ham _____ _____na cha bhavathi

5. vya:ghu:rnan_____ _____ _____ parikaro:

VI. Rearrange the words to reveal the slo:ka

1.naha	2. yath	3. saha	4. disathu
5. samasthe:	6. suragane:	7. mangalam	8. khinne
9. mu:la:	10. mu:lai	11. nayane:	12. santhatham
13.bhagava:n	14. na+aham	15. na+aham	16. mukhulitha
17. sapadi	18. ithi+e:vam	19. mu:lam	20. thyaktha+hasthe:
21. praduhu+a:si:th	22. bha:vasu:nye:	23. nacha:ham	24. bhavathi
25. Tha:drusaha	26. ithi	27. kari:ndre:	28. punaha
29. nakra	30. akra:nthe	31. na cha	32. ma:druse:shu

VII. Circle the odd man out

1. rattha:ngam, saram, asim, cha:pau, kaumo:daki, sakhe:tou, gambhi:ra

2. gaje:ndra, suragane:, rudathi, nakra, tha:rkshya, harihi

3. cloud, fire, sky, ocean, Na:ra:yana, blue sapphire mountain

4. Va:mana, Gaje:ndra, Draupadi, Sugri:va

5. Elephant, giraffe, monkey, lion, zebra

6. Protector, traitor, savior, originator, compassionate

7. Fish, seal, alligator, turtle, frog

8. Friends, sages, de:vathas, God, people

VIII. Analogy

1. Gaje:ndra Mo:kshanam is to eliminate bad dreams as _____ is to beautify thoughts.

2. Gra:ha is to crocodile as Karindre: is to _____.

3. Bhagawad Gi:tha is to Maha:bha:ratha as Gaje:ndra Mo:kshanam is t _____.

4. Devotee is to surrender as _____ is to protect.

5. Gaje:ndra is to Sri:Hari as Draupadi is to _____.

IX. One Word Answers

1. In which scripture do we find the story of Gaje:ndra?

   _____

2. Who was Gaje:ndra?

   _____

3. What is the vehicle of Lord Vishnu?

   _____

4. How did Gaje:ndra address God?

   _____

5. How does Lord show His assurance of protection?

   _____

6. What did Lord Vishnu use to protect Gaje:ndra?

_____

7. Who always helps us in times of need?

_____

X. Answer the following

1. From whom did Gaje:ndra seek help?

_____

_____

2. What does "na:ham na:ham nacha:ham" mean?

_____

_____

3. How did Lord Sri:Hari react to Gaje:ndra's prayer?

_____

_____

4. Why did Lord Sri:Hari rush to help Gaje:ndra?

_____

_____

5. What did you learn from Gaje:ndra Mo:kshanam story?

_____

_____

XI. Who am I?

a) I am a monkey but became a devotee of Lord. I jumped across the ocean to Lank
to search for Si:tha de:vi. Who am I?

_____

b) I am a ra:kshasa: by birth but became a devotee of Lord Na:ra:yana. Unfortunatel
my father hated Him very much. Lord protected me from the dangers my father pu
me in. Who am I?

_____

c) I am an elephant. One day, when I was playing with my family in the river, a
alligator attacked me. None of my family or friends could save me. It was onl
Lord Na:ra:yana who finally saved me. Who am I?

_____

d) I am the son of Lord Bramha and became a devotee of Lord Na:ra:yana. I have
vi:na in my hand and always sing 'Na:ra:yana Na:ra:yana'. Who am I?

_____

e) I was a prince. My step mother was cruel to me. My mom asked me to pray t
Lord Na:ra:yana. I went to the forest when I was five years old and did meditatio
God appeared and gave me a boon. I became a polestar. Who am I?

_____

XII. Complete the patterns by choosing the correct answer from pink boxes.

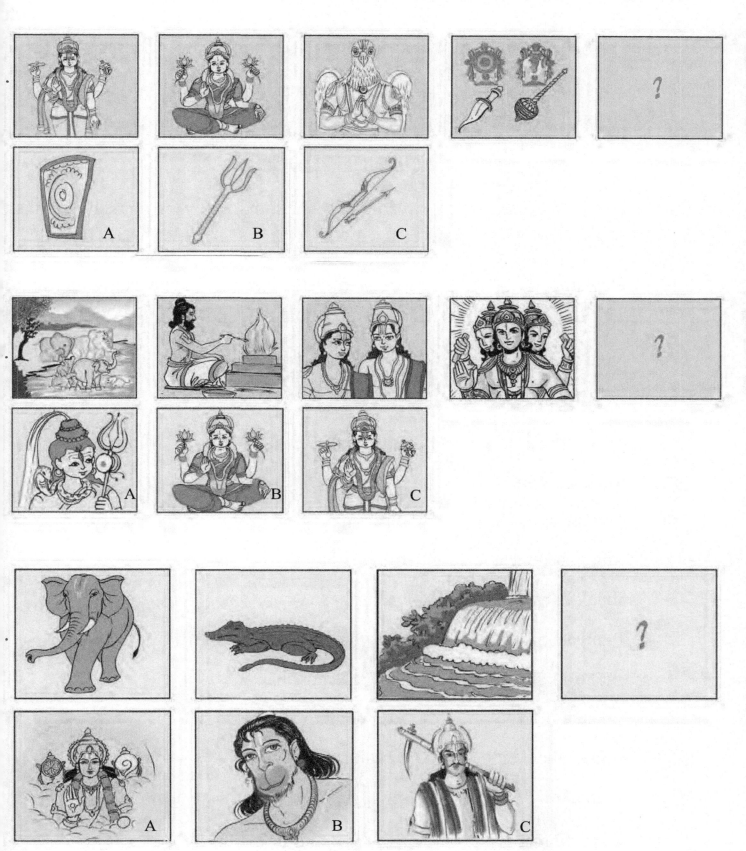

XIII. Amarako:sam

garudaha	=	tha:rkshyaha, garuthma:n, vainathe:yah khage:swaraha, naga:nthakaha, vishnuratthaha,
crocodile	=	gra:haha, nakraha, kumbhi:raha
bow	=	cha:paha, dhanuhu, sara:sanam, ishva:saha, ko:dandam, ka:rmukam
eye	=	nayanam, lo:chanam, ne:thram, chakshuhu, akshi:kshanam
elephant	=	gajaha, karihi, na:gaha, kunjaraha, va:ranaha, ibhah dvipaha, dwiradaha, hasthi:
hand	=	hasthaha, karaha, pa:nihi

XIV. nana:rttha:s

protecting	=	avathu, pa:thu, rakshathu

XV. Opposite Words

1. abhayam   X bhayam

2. khinnaha   X mudithaha

3. thyakthaha   X gruhi:thaha

4. bha:vasu:nyaha   X bha:vapu:rnaha

5. mukulitha nayanaha   X vikasitha nayanaha

6. rakshathu   X samharathu

7. gho:shaha   X nissabdaha

8. grahanam   X thya:gaha

9. a:kra:nthaha   X a:vishka:raha

XVI. A. Join syllables to get verbs in present tense and form sentences if possible.

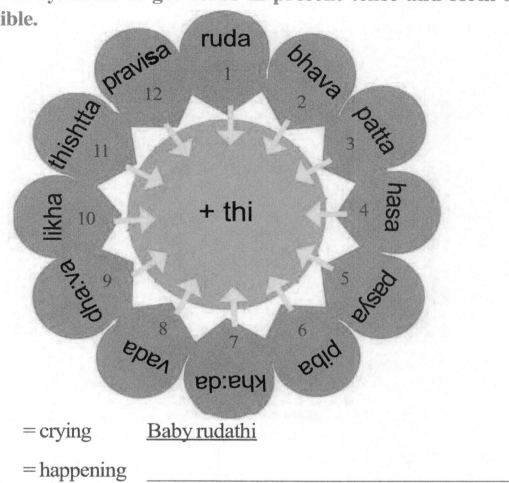

1. _____ = crying   <u>Baby rudathi</u>

2. _____ = happening   _____

3. _____ = reading   _____

4. _____ = laughing   _____

5. _____ = looking   _____

6. _____ = drinking   _____

7. _____ = eating   _____

8. _____ = telling   _____

9. _____ = running   _____

10. _____ = writing   _____

11. _____ = standing   _____

12. _____ = entering   _____

B. Join words and form sentences if possible.

Ex- de:v<u>a</u> + <u>i</u>ndraha: = de:v<u>e:</u>ndraha

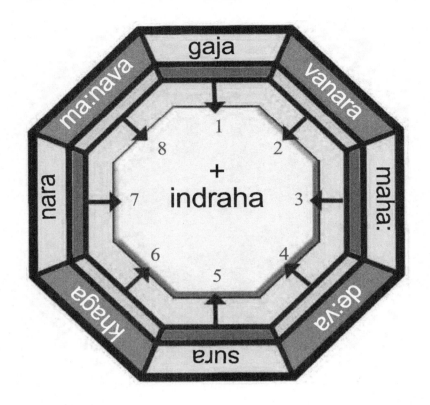

1. <u>gaje:ndraha</u>   = king of Elephants   _____

2. _____   = king of Monkeys   _____

3. _____   = king of de:vatha:s   _____

4. _____   = king of De:vatha:s   _____

5. _____   = king of de:vatha:s   _____

6. _____   = king of Birds   _____

7. _____   = king of humans   _____

8. _____   = king of humans   _____

Can you coin more words?

C. Join the words below with suffix 'indraha' to get the best persons among all.

Observe how the vowel is changing

i + i = i: a + i = e:

<u>kari:ndraha</u>

king of elephants

ravi_____

king of suns

giri_____

king of mountains

+ <u>i</u>ndraha

avi_____

king of poets i .e

Va:lmi:ki

hari_____

king of monkeys i .e

Sugri:va

yathi_____

king among the saints

i .e Ra:ma:nuja

D. Join the words and form sentences if possible. Observe the consonan
followed by vowels in the words below.

Ex. tha:rkshya<u>m</u>+ <u>a:</u>ruhya=tha:rkshya<u>ma:</u>ruhaya.

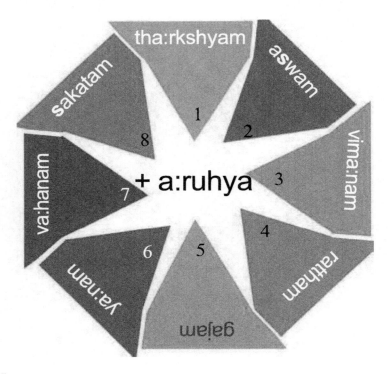

a:ruhya=climbed

1. _____ = after mounting on Garuda _____

2. _____ = after mounting on the horse back _____

3. _____ = after boarding on the flight _____

4. _____ = after climbing the chariot _____

5. _____ = after mounting on the elephant back _____

6. _____ = after getting into the vehicle _____

7. _____ = after getting into the car _____

8. _____ = after climbing the bullock cart _____

E. **Join the suffix 'ganaha' to get different groups and form sentences if possible.**

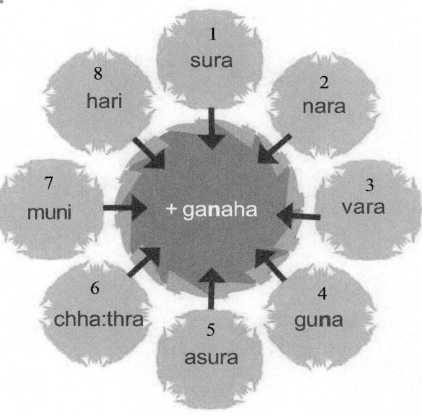

anaha = a group

1. _____ = group of de:vathas _____

2. _____ = group of people _____

3. _____ = group of best things _____

4. _____ = group of qualities _____

5. _____ = group of demons _____

6. _____ = group of students _____

7. _____ = group of sages _____

8. _____ = group of monkeys _____

F. **Join the syllables to get words showing comparisons and form sentences if possible.**

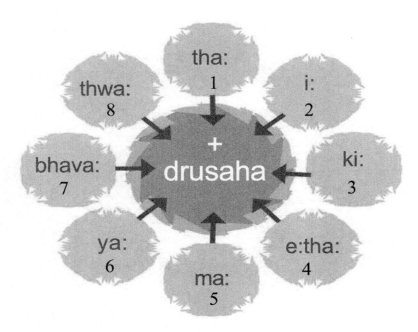

<u>drusaha</u> = equal to something

1. _____ = like that   <u>I need a book shelf tha: drusaha.</u>

2. _____ = like this   _____

3. _____ = like what?   _____

4. _____ = like this   _____

5. _____ = like me   _____

6. _____ = like what ever   _____

7. _____ = like you (with respect)   _____

8. _____ = like you (equal with age)   _____

XVII. What is wrong in this picture?

XVIII.   Connect Dots

XIX. Color this

Namaskaram

A:va:haya:mi

Udva:saya:mi

Mruga mudra

Sankalpam

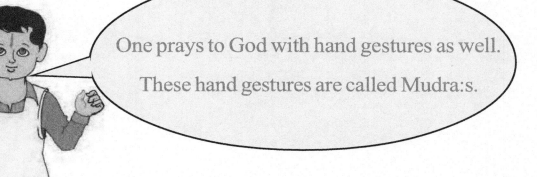

One prays to God with hand gestures as well.

These hand gestures are called Mudra:s.

XX.Spot 15 differences

XXI. Write the dialogues for the picture story below and color the pictures.

What is the moral of the story?

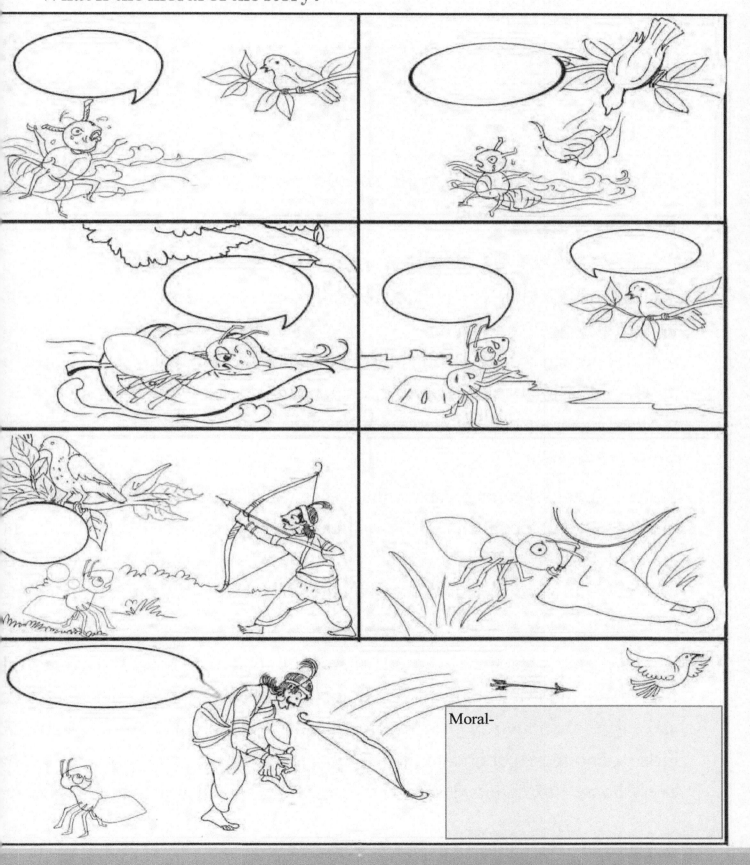

XXII. Do you remember?

In Module 1, you learned a slo:ka to avoid bad dreams. What is that slo:ka?

_____

_____

_____

_____

To avoid bad dreams, you should think about _____

_____, and _____

XXIII. Let us practice - Bhu:tha Yajna

The Universe is God's creation. Everything belongs to Him. Therefore God ha
bountiful concern and compassion for every living and non-living being in th
world. This can be seen in Gaje:ndra Mo:kshanam. God rushed from His divir
abode to Earth to save Gaje:ndra, an elephant. As everything belongs to Go
preserving and protecting plants, animals and Nature is one of the yajna:s calle
Bhu:tha Yajna.

Watering plants, keeping water in the open yard for pets/birds, hanging birds fee
in the backyard, feeding domestic animals, helping an injured bird or animal etc
are all activities of Bhu:tha Yajna. By performing Bhu:tha Yajna, we not on
protect Nature and creatures but also enjoy the beauty of them. So, don't spo
them. Don't abuse them.

Bhu:tha Yajna is practiced even today in remote villages in India, by decorating th
front porch of the houses using rice flour. Colors are mixed with rice flour. Line
and curves are drawn by girls in different patterns to form beautiful designs. Th
girls extend these patterns to the neighbor house's pattern to form a link. Thu
every house links up its design to the next house's design forming a chain ar

these extend to the next street. Thus the whole village is linked up like a chain with beautiful, colorful patterns. These rice flour patterns:

a)   Help the insects to get some food

b)   Make the entrance look colorful and attractive

c)   Help maintain friendly relationship with neighbors.

This Bhu:tha Yajna has been coined as a motto by Sri Chinna Jeeyar Swamiji "Serve All Beings as Service to God". Practice it everyday!

Identify various activities of Bhu:tha Yajna in the pictures below and color them.

. This is a traditional "Muggu". Color this.

C. A few people were crossing through a forest and saw people in slums who wer[e] without food, clothes, potable water and houses. They reported it to VT Sev[a] Head quarters. Our VT Seva volunteers are in the rescue operations. Identify ho[w] our volunteers can help them.

1. _____

2. _____

3. _____

XXIV.   Research Activity

1.   Concern for animals - Imagine somebody pricks you, how would you feel? If you prick someone how will he feel? Imagine you have a pet animal – a goat, a duck, a dog or a cat. If you prick them, what would be their reaction? If your friend kicks them, how would you feel? If somebody kicks you, how would your mom feel? If somebody kicks your brother or sister how would you feel?

Imagine if somebody cuts a chick or breaks an egg, how does its mom feel? Find the foods made of birds and animals. Do you like them?

2.   List the advantages of being a vegetarian vs. a meat eater.

Did you know? Elephant is the strongest animal on the earth and it is a pure vegetarian.

3.   List a few animals that were used in olden days for travelling.

4.   Krushna protected cows but killed a calf. He protected a bird but killed another bird. Justify his actions.

XXV. Project

Collect some pictures about our Swamiji's activities in protecting cows and other animals and paste on a board.

XXVI.   Game - Help baby elephant to reach its mother.

XXVII. Food for Thought

Describe in your own words the feelings of Gaje:ndra while he was praying to all
r help and when he was protected.

Slo:ka Thrayam

6. Slo:ka Thrayam

I. Choose the correct answer

1. _____ cannot be controlled.

   a) Our actions

   b) Our speech

   c) Our mind

   d) All the above

2. The almighty is called Lord Sri:manna:ra:yana because

   a) He is all pervading, external to all things in this Universe

   b) He permeates inside every object in this Universe

   c) everything depends upon Him

   d) all of the above

3. Sequence of activities mentioned in Slo:ka Thrayam

   a) Smara:mi, Nama:mi, Bhaja:mi

   b) Nama:mi, Smara:mi, Bhaja:mi

   c) Bhaja:mi, Nama:mi, Smara:mi

   d) Nama:mi, Bhaja:mi, Smara:mi

4. The first slo:ka quotes how God saved

   a) Dhruva

   b) Gaje:ndra

   c) Prahla:da

   d) Ambari:sha

5. Holy scriptures

   a) teach us Yo:ga: exercises

   b) describe how to live a healthy and peaceful life

   c) have stories only

   d) none of the above

6. The Sanskrit word "mu:rdhna" means
   a) with folded hands
   b) with head
   c) with knees
   d) with mind

7. Lord feels _____ when His devotees are saved.
   a) very pleased
   b) disappointed
   c) unconcerned
   d) none of the above

8. Lord's complexion in this stho:thra is compared to
   a) anjana:bham
   b) ni:la me:gham
   c) barhi pincha
   d) all of the above

9. Chanting Slo:ka Thrayam, we can cross
   a) the ocean
   b) samsa:ra
   c) Ganga: River
   d) none of the above

10. To get rid of bad dreams, chant
    a) Krushna:shtakam
    b) Slo:ka Thrayam
    c) Haryashtakam
    d) none of the above

II. **Fill in the blanks**

1. Grief is caused by our attachment due to _____.

2. I _____, _____ and _____ bow down to the divine lotus feet of Lord **Srimanna:ra:yana**.

3. God alone is the _____ that helps us in crossing the perilous _____called _____.

4. _____ alone is "Purusho:tthama".

5. The 3 powerful instruments everyone is blessed with are _____, _____ and _____.

6. In this stho:thra, the eyes of God are compared to _____.

7. _____ is done with Manas.

8. Nama:mi means _____

9. Smara:mi means _____

10. Bhaja:mi means _____

III. **Match the following**

1. smara:mi   a. cross the ocean called Naraka

2. bhaja:mi   b. remember Lord Sri:manna:ra:yana every morning

3. nama:mi   c. pray early in the morning

                     d. bow physically, mentally and verbally

                     e. eradicates sins

                     f. get rid of grief caused by ego

                     g. blesses us with courage

IV.   **Complete the following words**

1.   pa:___ ___ ___yana

2.   gra: ___ ___ ___ bhi ___ ___u:tha

3.   p___r___m___sy ___

4.   ___ ___ ___ ___:mi

5.   ma___ a___a:

6.   pr___v___n___

7.   pu___sa___a

8.   v___kthr___

9.   ___ ___ ___ ja:mi

10.   m___ ___ ___hi

V.   **Fill in the slo:ka blanks**

1.   chakra:yudham _____ _____
      pathra ne:thram

2.   pra:thar nama:mi_____ _____
      mu:rdhna:

3.   _____ naraka:rnava tha:ranasya

4.   _____ prana:sana karo: dhrutha _____
      _____

5.   _____ _____ paramasya pumsaha

VI. Rearrange the words to frame the slo:ka

1. nama:mi   2. pra:thaha   3. mu:rdhna: 4. manasa:

5. vachasa: 6. cha   7. pa:da   8. Na:ra:yanasya

9. pumsaha   10. paramasya   11. tha:ranasya   12. pa:ra:yanasya

13. yugalam   14. vipra   15. aravinda   16. naraka:rnava

17. pravana   18. pa:ra:yana

VII. Circle the odd man out

1. manas, va:k, ka:ya, ne:thra

2. smell, taste, digestion, sight, hearing, touch

3. harsh, satirical, critical, kind, rude, offensive, impolite, cruel

4. love, compassion, Na:ra:yana, generous, supreme, savior, ruler

5. boat, ship, Na:ra:yana, whale, cruise ships, cargo ship

6. Lo:kathraya guruhu, Harihi, Vipra, Purusho:ththama, Na:ra:yana

7. Garuda, bull, mouse, peacock, swan, snake

8. trio, triad, triplet, triple, dual, threefold

9. Naraka, grief, sorrow, pain, misery, woe, unhappiness

10. Naraka, krushnagathi, pre:yo:ma:rga, black path, suklagathi

VIII. Answer the following

1. Why does man commit various sins?

   _____

2. What are the three worlds?

   _____

3. Who is the ruler of the three worlds?

_____

4. How can we get rid of the grief caused by ego?

_____

5. How can we control the senses?

_____

6. Why is Na:ra:yana called 'Purusho:ththama'?

_____

IX. Label the pictures using words from the stho:thra

_____   _____   _____   _____

_____   _____

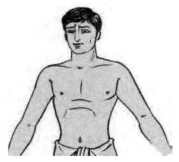

_____   _____   _____   _____   _____

X. Unscramble words from slo:kas

1) Hay   _____

2) Maid   _____

3) Math   _____

4) Kra:p   _____

5) Ko:sa   _____

XI. Do you remember?

In Module 1, you learnt the slo:ka below

ka:ye:na va:cha: manase:ndri yairva

buddhya:thma na:va prakruthe: svabha:va:th

karo:mi yadyath sakalam parasmai

na:ra:yana:ye:thi samarpaya:mi

This slo:ka mentions the three instruments required to do any activity – manas, ka:ya, and va:k.

What is an instrument called in Sanskrit? Fill the blanks to find the word.

k ___ r ___ **n** ___ m

XII.   Learn the words

manasa: =   with mind

vachasa: =   with words

mu:rdhna: =   with head

ka:ye:na   =   with body

hasthe:na   =   with hand

XIII.   Amarako:sam - Word Bank

ocean   = arnavaha, sa:garaha, sindhuhu, udadhihi, abdhihi, samudraha, rathna:karaha, va:ridhihi, jalanidhihi.

foot   = anghrihi, pa:daha, charanaha, path

world   = lo:kaha, jagath, vishtapam, bhuvanam

scholar = vipraha, dwijaha, bhu:suraha, bra:mhanaha

XIV.   Opposite words

1.   tharunaha   X   vruddhaha

2.   so:kaha   X   mo:daha

3.   narakaha   X   swargaha

4.   pra:thaha   X   sa:yam

XV.   **A. Join syllables with suffix 'thum' to get nouns and form sentences if possible.**

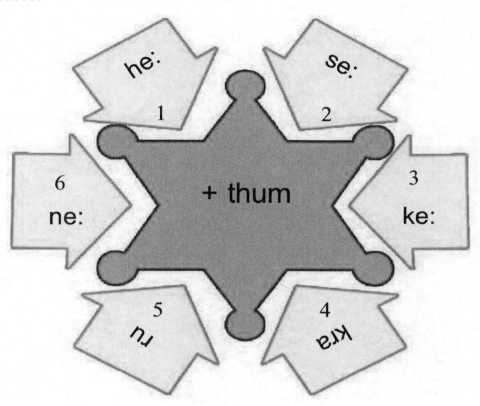

1. <u>he:thum</u>   = towards the cause/ reason <u>I can imagine the he:thum for pain.</u>

2. _____   = towards bridge _____

3. _____   = towards flag/a planet _____

4. _____   = towards ya:ga _____

5. _____   = towards the season _____

6. _____   = to take away _____

B. **Join syllables with suffix 'thum' to get verbs and get ready to do differe**
activities; and form sentences if possible.

Ex - patti +thum = pattithum-to read

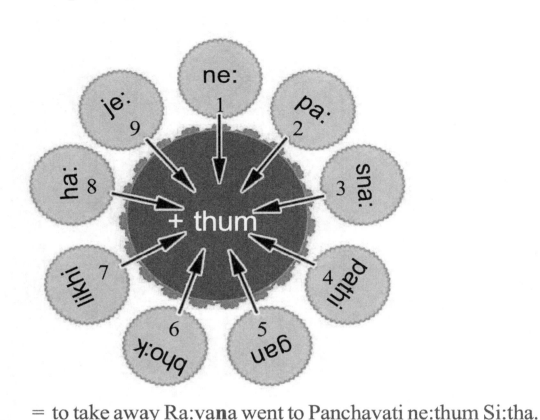

thum = to do

1. _____ = to take away Ra:vana went to Panchavati ne:thum Si:tha.

2. _____ = to drink _____

3. _____ = to bathe _____

4. _____ = to fall _____

5. _____ = to go _____

6. _____ = to eat _____

7. _____ = to write _____

8. _____ = to give up _____

9. _____ = to win _____

C. Join the nouns with suffix "he:thum" and form sentences if possible.

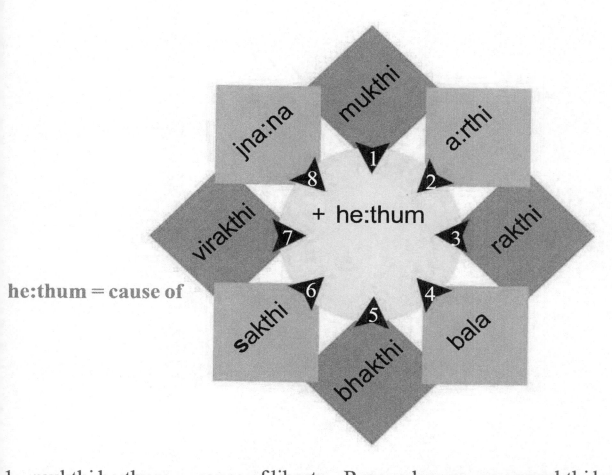

he:thum = cause of

1. <u>mukthi he:thum</u> = cause of liberty <u>Remember prayer as mukthi he:thum.</u>

2. _____ = cause of eagerness _____

3. _____ = cause of love   _____

4. _____ = cause of strength_____

5. _____ = cause of devotion _____

6. _____ = cause of energy   _____

7. _____ = cause of laziness _____

8. _____ = cause of knowledge _____

D. Join verb with the suffix to get activities in first person and form sentence if possible.

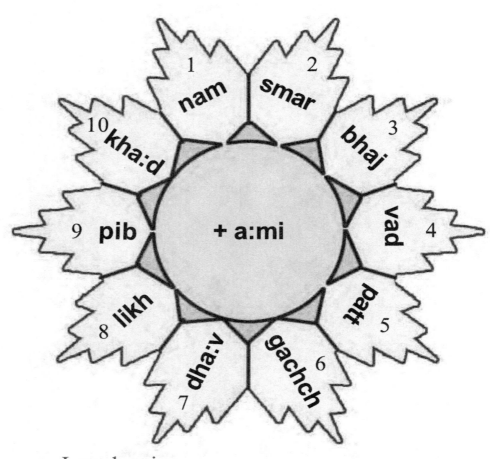

1. nama:mi   = I am bowing _____

2. _____   = I am remembering _____

3. _____   = I am serving _____

4. _____   = I am telling _____

5. _____   = I am reading _____

6. _____   = I am going _____

7. _____   = I am running/washing_____

8. _____   = I am writing _____

9. _____   = I am drinking _____

10. _____   = I am eating _____

E. Make compound words which describe the lotus like beauty form sentences if possible.

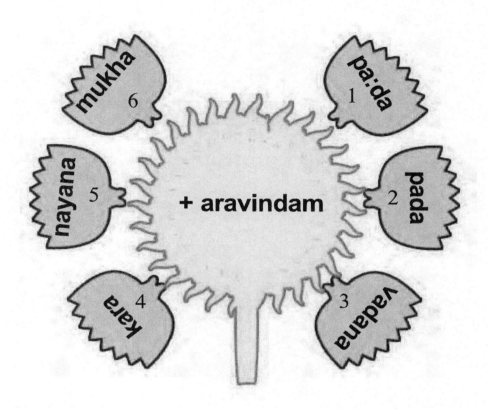

a:da+aravindam = pa:da:ravindam

1. pa:da:ravindam = lotus like foot <u>I surrender at the pa:daravindam of Krushna.</u>

2. _____ = lotus like foot _____

3. _____ = lotus like mouth _____

4. _____ = lotus like hand _____

5. _____ = lotus like eye _____

6. _____ = lotus like face _____

F. **Make compound words to pacify certain things.**

1. maha:rthi sa:nthyai   = to pacify great misery

2. _____ = to pacify anger

3. _____ = to pacify ignorance

4. _____ = to pacify fear

5. _____ = to pacify fire

6. _____ = to pacify grief

7. _____ = to pacify hunger

8. _____ = to pacify thurst

G Make compound words and write the meanings.

x - **gra:ha abhibhu:thaha gajaha** - an elephant captured by a crocodile

gra:ha	+		gajaha
duhkha (sorrow)	+	**abhibhu:thaha +**	manaha
kro:dha (anger)	+		jna:nam
me:gha (cloud)	+		su:ryaha

1. _____

2. _____

3. _____

4. _____

5. _____

6. _____

7. _____

8. _____

H. **Make compound words which tell us about somebody who wore som**
object and form sentences if possible.

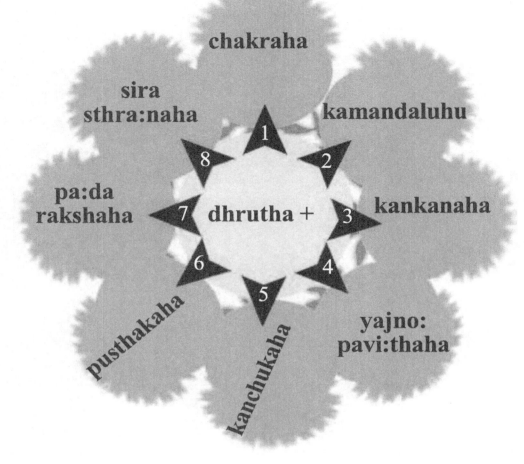

1. <u>dhrutha chakraha</u>   =   one who holds chakra   <u>Vishnu stands dhrutha chakraha</u>

2. _____   =   one who holds wooden pot _____

3. _____   =   one who wore bracelet   _____

4. _____   =   one who wore sacred thread_____

5. _____   =   one who wore shirt   _____

6. _____   =   one who holds book   _____

7. _____   =   one who wore footwear   _____

8. _____   =   one who wore helmet   _____

I. Form compound words to know different abodes and form sentences if possible.

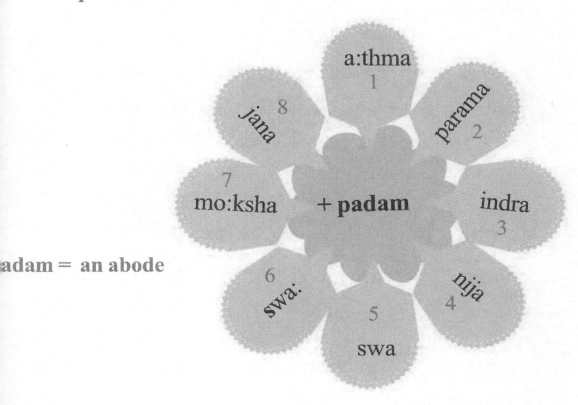

adam = an abode

1. <u>a:thama padam</u> = my place   <u>After a long journey, I reached</u>

                                <u>a:thmapadam.</u>

2. _____ = Supreme abode of God   _____

3. _____ = Indra's abode   _____

4. _____ = one's own abode   _____

5. _____ = self abode   _____

6. _____ = abode of dogs   _____

7. _____ = utlimate abode of bliss   _____

8. _____ = a district   _____

J. **Join the words to get a few pairs. Can you guess the meanings of those words?**

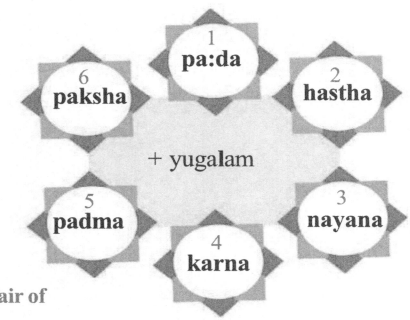

Yugalam = pair of

1. pa:da yugalam   =   _____

2. _____   =   _____

3. _____   =   _____

4. _____   =   _____

5. _____   =   _____

6. _____   =   pair of wings/fortnight

K. Join the words to get groups which contain 3 things in it and write the meanings.

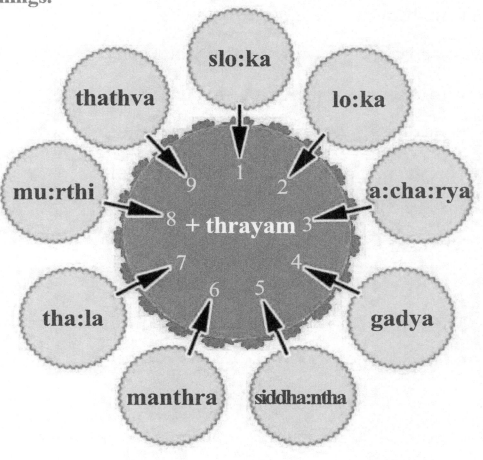

1. _____ = _____

2. _____ = _____

3. _____ = _____

4. _____ = group of three prose

5. _____ = group of three doctrines

6. _____ = _____

7. _____ = three claps

8. _____ = _____

9. _____ = group of three realities

XVI. Learn Colors

pi:tha:mbaram   = garment in yellow color

sukla:mbaram   = garment in white color

krushna:mbaram   = garment in black color

ni:la:mbaram   = garment in blue color

ka:sha:ya:mbaram   = garment in saffron color

Now can you say who wears what?

a) Krushna   1) sukla:mbaram

b) Our Swa:mi:ji   2) pi:tha:mbaram

c) Vishwakse:na   3) ka:sha:ya:mbaram

d) Sani de:vatha   4) krushna:mbaram

XVII. Learn this slo:ka

nama:mi na:ra:yana pa:da pankajam

karo:mi na:ra:yana pu:janam sada:

vada:mi na:ra:yana na:ma nirmalam

smara:mi na:ra:yana thathvam avyayam

I always bow at the lotus feet of Lord Narayana

I always worship Narayana

I always chant the divine name of Narayana

I always meditate on the eternal nature of Narayana

Is the above slo:ka conveying a message similar to slo:ka thrayam?

_____

XVIII.   Color

XIX. Connect Dots

XX. Identify how many musical instruments are used by the Jai Srimannarayan Bhajan group. Also, there are 6 flutes in the picture. Can you find them?

XI. Spot 15 differences

XXII. Let us practice

Become a Better Citizen

We are all gifted with three powerful instruments- the body, mind and the power of speech. If we use these instruments properly, they become perfect tools and enable us to do good deeds. However, we tend to misuse these instruments. We do things that not only harm others but also harm ourselves.

For example, we can take the analogy of a matchstick. Matchstick not only burns objects close to it, but also the stick on which it depends. Similarly, when we misuse our instruments, we bring grief to others and also ourselves. This is because we listen to our senses and eventually become their slaves instead of having them under our control. As a result, we lose focus, become lazy, impatient, waste time, and become unhealthy and passive. We will neither be successful in life nor become good citizens.

VT Seva is conducting a Personality Development Camp. They are planning to distribute a daily practice chart to all participants. Can you help them create one using the example below?

Daily Practice Chart

Action	Sun	Mon	Tue	Wed	Thu	Fri	Sa
Ex: Did I hurt anyone's feelings by speaking harshly? (Yes or No)							

XXIII. Mark ✓ if 'manas', 'va:k', or 'ka:ya' is used properly. Else mark ✗. Also identify what instrument is used.

XXIV. Game

Ma:nasi wants to meditate on God for 10 minutes. But her senses are tempting h
to do different things. Help Ma:nasi's manas to concentrate on God by playing this gan

Throw dice.

If you throw 1, Ma:nasi's manas will think of God and you will win.

If you throw 2, her friends call her and say 'Hey let us go to a movie'.

If you throw 3, classmates call her saying 'Get ready in 5 min. We are going to a picni

If you throw 4, Ma:nasi wants to watch TV and listen to music

If you throw 5, Ma:nasi wants to play vedio games

If you throw 6, give Ma:nasi another chance to meditate on God

XXV. Think

 Play Tug of war game. How did you feel when others were pulling you while you were trying to resist?

 Imagine you are surrounded by wolves. There is no way to escape unless you climb a tree or someone comes to your rescue.

 A similar situation occurs when your mind pulls you towards some bad things. Put your manas on God and you will be saved !

XXVI. Food for thought

When you visit any temple, what is that you do first? Is it smara:mi, nama:mi or bhaja:mi in your experience? Is there a particular sequence?

> When you are attracted to something, all three things – smara:mi, nama:mi and bhaja:mi will follow. Just experience!

Parathva:di Panchakam

7. Parathva:di Panchakam

I. Choose the correct answer

1. Parathva:di Panchakam has
    a) five slo:ka:s
    b) two slo:ka:s
    c) seven slo:ka:s
    d) none of the above

2. Identify the divine quality of Lord
    a) all pervasiveness
    b) all knowing
    c) all powerful
    d) all of the above

3. How many incarnations did God take?
    a) 10
    b) 108
    c) 18
    d) unlimited

4. _____describes the divine forms of Lord.
    a) Slo:ka Thrayam
    b) Slo:ka Dvayam
    c) Parathva:di Panchakam
    d) Archira:di

5. Another name of Anantha is _____.
    a) Hanuma:n
    b) Prahla:da
    c) A:dise:sha
    d) Ambari:sha

6. Vyuha Va:sudeva has _____ Vyuha:s.

    a) 3

    b) 4

    c) 5

    d) 8

7. Lord is called Vishnu because

    a) He controls everything in this Universe

    b) He is inside and outside all animate and inanimate objects

    c) He is supreme

    d) All of the above

8. An example of Divya De:sam is

    a) Sri: Rangam

    b) Thirumala

    c) Ka:nchipuram

    d) All of the above

9. Lord takes avatha:ras

    a) with so much pain

    b) just like child's play

    c) with care and hardwork

    d) none of the above

10. Example of Vibhava form

    a) Sri: Rangana:ttha

    b) Va:sude:va

    c) Sri Ra:ma

    d) Paramapada Na:ttha

II. Fill in the blanks

1. God resides in the hearts of _____ limiting Himself to the size of their _____.

2. God dwells as Aniruddha possessing infinite _____ and _____.

3. God dwells as Pradyumna possessing infinite ——————— and ——————.

4. He dwells as Sankarshana possessing infinite ——————— and ——————.

5. The word Parathvam means ——————————————.

6. According to A:gama:s, there are _____ divine abodes of Lord.

7. The supreme abode of Lord is called _____.

8. Parathva:di Panchakam was composed by _____.

9. The indweller form of God is called _____.

10. The form of God in milky ocean is known as _____.

III. Match the following

1. Parava:sude:va

a) takes incarnations on this Earth to protect good people and eliminate bad people

2. Vyu:ha

b) who lives in Paramapadam

3. Vibhava

c) who is seated inside all animate and inanimate objects

4. Antharya:mi

d) existing in the deity form in temples and houses of devotees

5. Archa:

e) lives in Milky ocean planning for creation, protection and destruction

IV. Fill in slo:ka blanks

1. nirmala _____ _____ ghana swaru:pam

2. _____ _____ se:vyam _____ bho:
   nilayam

   sri: va:sude:vam bhaje:

3. a:mo:de: bhuvane: _____ _____ _____
   sankarshanam

4. ve:da:n ve:shana _____ bharana

5. sri:rangastthala _____ _____
   sathe:shtothare:

V. Unscramble

1. I G O Y : _____

2. DA:S A _____

3. PAI _____

4. LAAAM _____

VI. Rearrange the words to form a slo:ka

1. namaha	2. sri:sa:ya	3. archa:ru:pinam

4. sathe:shtothare: sttha:ne: 6. sada: 7. ve:nkata:dri

8. cha   9. gra:ma   10. sri:rangastthala   11. nike:thane:shu

12. karigirya:dau 13. sa:nnidhya 14. akhilava:nchitha:n

15. archaka:bhimathithaha   16. pu:ja:m cha   17. svi:kurvathe:

18. vitharathe: 19. ma:se:dushe: 20. vigraham

21. thasmai

VII. True or False

1. The Archa: form of Lord is less powerful than the Lord in Paramapadam.

2. Lord takes the form of a deity on devotees' request.

3. Sri: Ra:ma deity at home is a Vibhava form of Lord.

4. Thirumala is a divya de:sam.

5. Only Nithya:s and Mukhtha:s serve the Lord in Paramapadam.

VIII. Find the odd man out

1. jna:na, sakthi, bala, aiswarya, vi:rya, the:jas, nirmala

2. para, vyu:ha, archa:, pa:tha:la, vibhava, antharya:mi

3. sankha, bhanu, chakra, sa:rngam, gada, khadga

4. a:moda, pramo:da, sammo:da, viraja

5. vi:rya, the:jas, absorbtion, creation

6. bala, aiswarya, protection, destruction

7. jna:na, sakthi, creation, dissolution

8. Va:mana, Ra:ma, Krushna, Vara:ha, Garuda

9. Vara:ha, Mathsya, Narasimha, Ku:rma, Ra:ma

10. sura, nara, thiryak, sttha:vara, de:vatha

11. birds, fish, insects, animals, trees

12. shrubs, trees, creepers, grass, plants, birds

13. agni, Indra, Va:yu, Varuna, Krushna

14. Ve:das, Purusha:rththa:s, Vyu:ha, divya desams

15. Sri Vaikunttam, Paramapadam, Parama:ka:sam, apara:jitha, Vyu:ha

IX. Analogy

1. Ku:rma is to turtle as _____ is to fish.

2. Vara:ha is to boar as _____ is to lion.

3. Vara:ha is to Hiranya:ksha as Narasimha is to _____

4. Sri:Hari is to Gaje:ndra as _____ is to earth.

5. A:mo:da is to Aniruddha as Pramo:da is to _____.

7. Narasimha is to Prahla:da as Va:mana is to _____.

8. Sammo:da is to Sankarshana as A:mo:da is to _____.

9. Sakthi is to Aniruddha as The:jas is to _____.

10. Creation is to Aniruddha as absorption is to _____.

11. Supreme abode is to parama:ka:sam as Hell is to _____

12. Muktha:s is to liberated souls as nithya:s is to _____.

13. Ra:ma is to Vibhava as Rangana:ttha is to _____.

14. Haryashtakam is to Prahla:da as Parathva:di Panchakam is to _____

15. Thirumala is to Ve:nkata:dri as Ka:nchipuram is to _____.

X. One word answers

1. What is the administrative place of Lord Na:ra:yana?

   _____

2. Who ploughed the river Ka:lindi?

   _____

3. In which form does lord reside in everyone's heart?

   _____

4. Who supported the Mount Mandara?

    _____

5. How many divya de:sams do we have?

    _____

6. Which quality of Lord is exhibited in archa: form?

    _____

7. Who resides in Sammo:da?

    _____

8. Who resides in Pramo:da?

    _____

9. Who resides in A:moda?

    _____

10. What is the most accessible form of Lord for us?

    _____

11. From where does Lord manage creation?

    _____

12. To whom is God visible as "Antharya:mi"?

    _____

13. From where does Lord manage protection?

    _____

14. Who absorbs the whole universe back into Him?

    _____

15. What are the benefits of chanting Parathva:di Panchakam?

    _____

X1. Answer the following

1. Describe the 6 divine attributes of the Supreme Lord?

   _____

   _____

2. Name the 4 categories of creatures.

   _____

   _____

XII. Opposites

nirmalam	X	pankilam
jna:ni	X	ajna:ni
srushtihi	X	samharaha
sada:	X	e:kada
anthaha	X	bahihi
anuhu	X	bruhath
ujjwalam	X	mla:nam
udayan	X	asthamayan
unmu:lanam	X	ro:panam
sa:nnidhyam	X	viyo:gaha
uththamam	X	adhamam

XIII.   Do you know the names of fingers in a hand

angushttaha   =   thumb

tharjani: =   pointed finger

madhyama: =   middle finger

ana:mika: =   ring finger

kanishttika: =   little finger

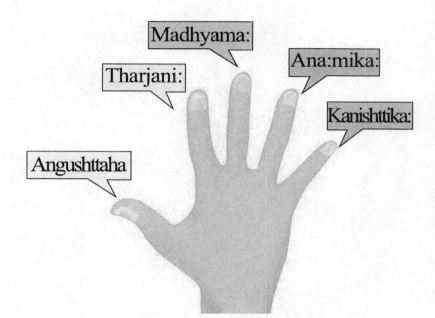

XIV.   A. Join the phrases to climb/ occupy certain position.

Ex- vyu:ha+adhishttitha +va:sude:vaha = vyu:ha:dhishttitha va:sude:vaha

vyu:ha		va:sude:vaha
gagana		chandraha
simha:sana	adhishttitha	ra:maha
vruksha	to climb/ occupy	khagaha
vima:na		ba:lakaha
rattha		ra:jaha

1. _____   4. _____

2. _____   5. _____

3. _____   6. _____

B. Join the words to get holy places

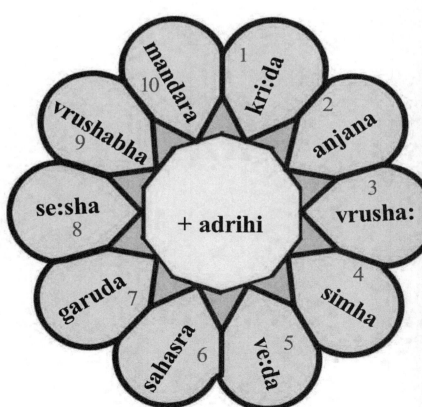

1. _____

2. _____

3. _____

4. _____

5. _____

6. _____

7. _____

C. Join the words to get the names of mountains

1. kri:da + adrihi = kri:da:drihi

2. _____

3. _____

4. _____

5. _____

6. _____

7. _____

8. _____

9. _____

10. _____

D. **Here are the leaders of certain groups. Make sentences if possible.**

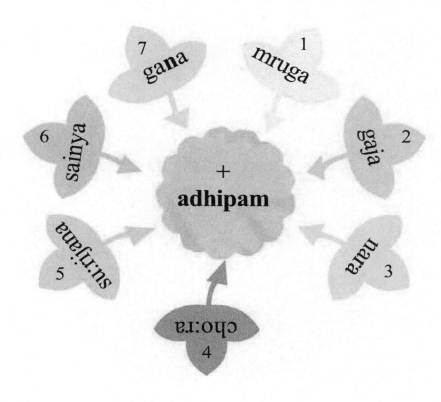

dhipam = towards the leader

1. <u>mruga:dhipam</u> = towards the leader of animals <u>Look at mruga:dhipam.</u>

2. _____ = towards the leader of elephants _____

3. _____ = towards the leader of men _____

4. _____ = towards the leader of thieves _____

5. _____ = towards theleader of de:vathas _____

6. _____ = towards the leader of army_____

7. _____ = towards the leader of the group_____

E. Join siffix 'nam' to get words describing one who is doing some activity in 2nd person and make sentences if possible.

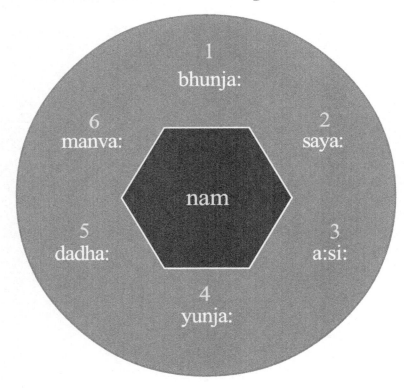

1. <u>bhunja:nam</u>   = to the one who is eating <u>I approached Krushna bhunja:nam butte</u>

2. _____   = towards the one who is sleeping_____

3. _____   = towards the one who is sitting_____

4. _____   = towards the one who is attaching_____

5. _____   = towards the one who is wearing_____

6. _____   = towards the one who is thinking_____

F.   Join the syllables to get rhyming words and make sentences if possible.

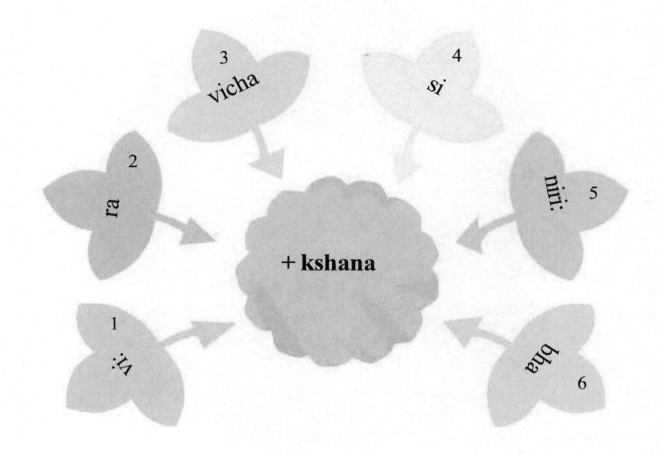

1. <u>vi:kshana</u>   = observing   <u>Hanuman's Lanka vi:kshana</u>

2. _____   = protection   _____

3. _____   = skillful   _____

4. _____   = training   _____

5. _____   = waiting   _____

6. _____   = eating   _____

G. Join siffix 'nam' to get words describing one who is doing some activity

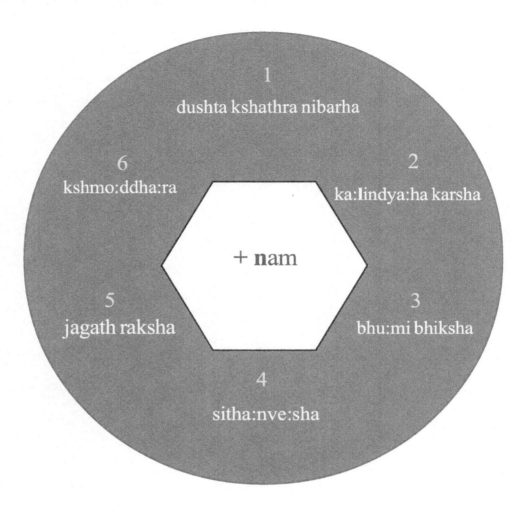

Inside circle:

1
dushta kshathra nibarha

6
kshmo:ddha:ra

2
ka:lindya:ha karsha

+ **n**am

5
jagath raksha

3
bhu:mi bhiksha

4
sitha:nve:sha

1. _____ = controlling evil kings

2. _____ = digging the cannal for river Ka:lindi

3. _____ = begging for ground

4. _____ = searching for Si:tha

5. _____ = protecting the world

6. _____ = lifting the earth

H. Join the words to know what is in them

chathurvide: 1

hrudaye: 2

chara:chare: 3

shu

loke: 4

ambhakthe: 5

jani 6

1. _____

2. _____

3. _____

4. _____

5. _____

6. _____

7. _____

XV.   Learn Numbers

Numbers-Sankhya:ha

1	2	3	4	5
:kam	dve	thri:ni	chathva:ri	pancha

6	7	8	9	10
hat	saptha	ashtau	nava	dasa

XVI. Draw various flowers Ananth A:lava:n is using to make a garland for Lord Venkate:swara. Write the different types of flowers he is using. Also count the number of each kind of flowers he used in sanskrit?

XVII.   Find 15 differences

XVIII.   Find na:ga:bharanam, Lakshmi devi, Padmavathi devi, sankha, chakra,
khadgam, sacred thread, abhaya hastha

IX. Steps to pray in a temple

1. A:gachcha:mi
2. Praksha:laya:mi
3. Pradakshanam karo:mi
4. Pranama:mi
5. De:vam darsaya:mi
6. Nama:mi
7. Thi:rttham svi:karo:mi
8. Upavisa:mi
9. Bhaja:mi
10. Prasa:dam svi:karo:mi
11. Kha:da:mi
12. Ghachcha:mi

Now label the above actions in the picture below.

1._____   2._____   3._____

4._____

5._____

6._____

7._____

8._____

9._____

10._____

11._____

12._____

XX. What is wrong in these pictures?

XXI. **To whom do these belong**

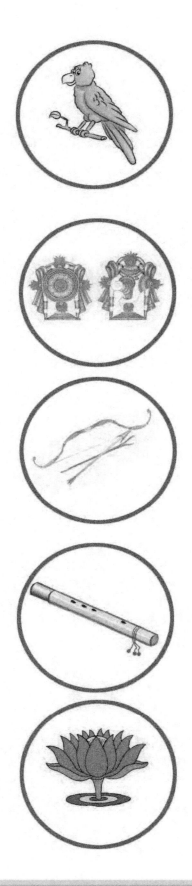

XXII. Label the following Vibhava avatha:ras and the purpose of the avatha:ras

Ex: Name: <u>Kurma Avathara</u>
Cause: to <u>support the mountain Mandara</u>

Name _____
Cause _____

Name _____
Cause _____

Name _____
Cause _____

Name _____
Cause _____

Name _____
Cause _____

Name _____

Cause _____

Name _____

Cause _____

Name _____

Cause _____

Name _____

Cause _____

XXIII. Research Activity

✤ Identify how many roles you have in your family and in your school.

✤ In your home, your father is the controller. In your county, the Superintendent is the controller. Mayor is the controller for your city and President is the controller of your country. Each country has a President but all the Presidents are controlled by God. A President can stay at one place at a time where as God can stay everywhere at a time.

List the different countries and their Presidents.

XXIV. Label below places in the map:

a) Sri:rangam b) Badarina:th c) Dwa:raka d)Thirumala e) Swamiji's Ashram – Divyasa:ketham in Hyderabad f) Ka:nchipuram g) Melkote h)Brinda:van

XXV. **Learn more**

Divya De:sam is a place where great people lived. There are12 a:lwa: and many a:cha:rya:s. Places which were glorified and sung by them ar called Divya De:sams.

There are 108 such major Divya De:sams. Two diyva de:sams namely th Paramapadam and the Milky Ocean cannot be seen right now. The othe 106 divyade:sams can be seen in Bha:rath. Sri:rangam, Thirumala Badrina:th, Dwa:raka, Sri:villiputtu:r are a few among them.

XXVI. **Let us practice**

A. **Protecting Our Heritage**

India is a land filled with beautiful, historic, and spiritual centers in th form of temples. These ancient temples have been built centuries ag These are not only artistic, environmentally friendly, having majesti architecture, but also are great learning hubs. Temples were focal point for passing our 'samprada:yam' to future generations.

The word 'Samprada:yam' has three parts in it - da:yam, prada:yan samprada:yam.

- da:yam   – ancestral property

- prada:yam   – passed on to us undisturbed

- samprada:yam – passed on to us unpolluted

This word 'samprada:yam' is used to talk about the spiritual and intellectua property.

Unfortunately, due to negligence, and under the pretense of modernization, these splendid structures aren't cared for properly. But, we must remember that it is our duty to protect our rich heritage. Let's join hands to save our temples.

In the below picture, a few people are destroyed a 600 year old colonnade in a temple as part of a beautification project. What would you do to fix it?

1. _____

2. _____

3. _____

B. Surrender Yourself for the cause

☞ Do service. Surrender yourself to the cause, focus on the goal and kee[p] doing service. See the result of it yourself!

☞ If you believe in the cause, surrender yourself to the cause and work wit[h] team spirit, you will achieve good results in the work you are doin[g]. While working in a team, people may have different opinions, the workin[g] style may be different; some may work fast while others might be slow[.] Do not discourage them. Work along with them patiently.

☞ If your cause is divine, surrender yourself to God. If it is a social caus[e] surrender yourself to the society

C. VT Seva volunteers are participating the "Clean a Lane' project. Is it a soci[al] cause or divine cause? If you are leading this project, list 5 things you woul[d] do as a leader to make this project successful.

If I am the project lead for 'Clean a Lane' project, I would

1. _____

2. _____

4. _____

5. _____

When you look at the deity (Archa:Vigraha) next time, just **recognize** that what you are looking at is the Supreme God with all **6 divine** qualities right there in front of you!

Archira:di

8. Archira:di

I. **Choose the correct answer**

1. What are the two paths for the soul?
   a) black path and white path
   b) sre:yo: ma:rga and pre:yo: ma:rga
   c) sukla gathi and krushna gathi
   d) all of the above

2. A soul will travel through white path when
   a) one loves materialistic objects
   b) one finds the directions to paramapadam
   c) one surrenders oneself to Lord
   d) none of the above

3. When soul enters the black path
   a) all desires are fulfilled
   b) it will be very happy
   c) will be stuck in the body subjected to cycle of life and death
   d) reaches divine abode

4. Divine abode
   a) is filled with divine bliss
   b) has lots of money
   c) is full of miseries and troubles
   d) all of the above

5. A:cha:rya reveals the shre:yo ma:rga to a disciple through
   a) initiation of Ashta:kshari: manthra
   b) Ve:das
   c) yo:ga and exercises
   d) none of the above

6. Goal of every soul must be

   a) to be healthy

   b) to earn money

   c) to gain knowledge

   d) to attain eternal bliss

7. Ashta:kshari: manthra reveals

   a) how to earn more and be rich

   b) how to be healthy

   c) the realization that Sriyahpathi is the cause and effect of this whole universe

   d) none of the above

8. Meditating on Ashta:kshari: manthra gives us a clear understanding of

   a) Nature, Prakruthi

   b) Souls

   c) Lord

   d) all of above

9. The moment one realizes and surrenders to Lord through guru, one's

   a) pra:rabdha karma and sanchitha karma are burnt to ashes

   b) sanchitha karma and a:ga:mi karma are burnt to ashes

   c) a:ga:mi karma and pra:rabdha karma are burnt to ashes

   d) none of the above

10. The Lord, from the heart of the devotee as _____ leads him showing the way out to eternal worlds.

   a) Suhrud

   b) Ha:rda

   c) Na:da

   d) none of the above

II. Fill in the blanks

1. The first step to attain liberation is to be in the company of _____

2. _____ guides one in realizing the Self, the Nature and the Suprem
    Lord.

3. The pre:yo: ma:rga is fixed for those who do not always think of ——————
    _____

4. If one constantly thinks of the ——————————————one's ——————
    ——bondage will be broken completely.

5. Our future is the result of our own ————————————————

6. If we chant Parama:rttha Slo:ka Dvayam regularly, ——————————
    Himself will chant it on our behalf when we are departing the world.

III. Complete the words

1. sri:_ _ _

2. praksh_:c_

3. a_ugr_h_

4. ar_h_h_

5. dh_ny_h_

IV. Fill In slo:ka blanks

1. ———————————————— bhava nisspruho: ——————————
    —— mukha:th —————————————— prapadya:thmava:n

2. ——————-—————————— labdha madhya——————
    ——————-—— dva:ra:d bahir nirgathaha

3. ———————————————————— upe:thya nithyam ajadam

4. ——————————— samava:pya ——————————— samam

5. pra:thar nithya:nu_____ _____
mumukshubhihi

V. Rearrange the words to frame the slo:ka

1. varado:bravi:th
2. samkshiptham
3. slo:ka

4. mumukshubihi
5. dvaye:na
6. suvyaktham

7. pra:thaha
8. nithya:nu
9. parama:rttham

10. sandhe:yam

VI. Circle the odd man out

1. sanchitham, karma, a:ga:mi, pra:rabdha

2. va:tha, amsumath, Indra, glau, pa:tha:la, varuna

3. dina, pu:rva paksha, shat udang ma:sa, abda, Indra

4. Ganga:, Viraja, Airummadam, Go:da:vari

5. Bliss, joy, happiness, misery, compassion

6. Garuda, Anantha, Sudarsana, Bramha, Sri:devi, Bhu:de:vi

7. guru, a:cha:rya, shishya

8. sorrow, problems, joy, tension, misery

VII. Analogy

1. Sins is to pre:yo:marga as surrendering is to _____

2. sukla gathi is to paramapada as krushna gathi is to _____

3. nithya is to pure soul as muktha is to _____

4. sukla gathi is to white path as krushna gathi is to _____

5. Enlighted people is to good thoughts as evil people is _____

6. Person with good qualities is to gunava:n as self realized person is _____

7. Future karma is to a:ga:mi as present karma is to _____

8. _____ is Jan 15th to July 14th as Dakshina:ya is to July 15th to Jan 14th.

9. Indra is to Indra lo:ka as Bramha is to _____

10. _____paksha is to waxing moon as uththara paksha is to wani moon.

VIII. Short Answers

1. What is the destination of white path?

    _____

2. Who composed Parama:rttha Slo:ka Dvayam?

    _____

3. Which chapter in Bhagawad Gi:tha reveals secrets of sukla gathi a krushna gathi?

    _____

4. Through which vein does the soul start its journey?

    _____

5. How many divine abodes does the liberated soul cross?

    _____

6. What is a liberated soul called?

_____

7. When does the soul shed the subtle body?

_____

8. Name the pool in Paramapada in which the 'muktha' bathes.

_____

9. Who touches the soul before entering the eternally glowing Paramapada?

_____

10. Which path is the best path?

_____

IX. **Answer the following**

1. What are the three kinds of ka:rmic records? Explain with an example illustrating each category?

_____

_____

2. How is pra:rabdha karma cleared?

_____

_____

3. List the differences between a nithya:, a muktha: and a baddha:.

_____

_____

4. Name the abodes the soul crosses through before entering Paramapada

    _____

    _____

5. Name the state in which one will be eternally happy?

    _____

    _____

6. Why do we need to constantly think about the "sre:yo: ma:rga"?

    _____

    _____

7. Describe the journey of a liberated soul till it leaves the body?

    _____

    _____

8. Describe the process of journey of the soul right from leaving this body
    until it reaches the Lord in paramapadam?

    _____

    _____

9. Describe paramapada.

    _____

    _____

10. Write five differences between naraka lo:ka and paramapada.

    _____

    _____

X. Rearrange the jumbled pictures as per the journey of soul.

XI. Dear friends, can you identify the places I visited?

1. This location is a junction with many routes leading to different lo:k
   Where am I? _____

2. Bramha and Saraswathi received me with honors at their place. Where a
   I? _____

3. I travelled on Garuda, and reached the most magnificent and beautif
   area. Where am I? _____

4. I took bath in this pool with a divine body. Where am I? _____

5. I was received with honors by de:vathas and Indra at this place. Where a
   I? _____

XII. Learn the words

anthaha	=	inside
bahihi	=	outside
adhaha	=	down
sarvathra	=	everywhere
upari	=	on the top
adhaha	=	under

XIII. Amarako:sam

1. knowledge = ma:ya, vayunam, jna:nam,

2. attachment = bhavaha, samsa:raha

3. air = va:thaha, va:yuhu, pavanaha, ma:thariswa:, maruth,
   gandhavahaha

4. lightening   = vidyuth, tatith, kshana prabhaha, chanchala, chapala:, hra:dini:,sauda:mini:

6. god of water   = varunaha, prache:thaha, appathihi, ya:dasa:mpathihi

7. indra   = indraha , maruthwa:n, pa:kasa:sanaha:, vrudhhas sravaha, purandaraha

XIV. Opposite Words

satsangaha	X	dussangaha
samam	X	vishamam
sangaha	X	nissangaha/thya:gaha
ma:nusham	X	ama:nusham
kshayam	X	akshayam

XV. Learn More-Definitions

1. Life- Journey of a soul through the body.

2. Souls dwell in three stages.

    a.   muktha = one who got liberation from karmic bondage

    b.   baddha = a soul with karmic bondage taking birth in different bodies

    c.   nithya= who resides always with God.

3. Mumukshu- One who seeks liberation from karmic bondage

4. Bhubhukshu- One who seeks worldly pleasures

5. Sathsang - company of good people or spiritual masters or devotees

6. Karma - records of deeds committed by a soul

XVI. A. Make compound words and make sentences.

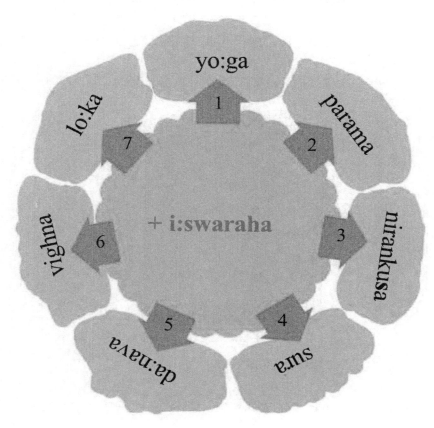

Ex. <u>yo:ga+i:swaraha</u> = <u>yo:ge:swaraha</u>

1. <u>yo:ge:swaraha</u> = <u>master of yo:ga</u>   <u>Mr. Hari is yoge:swaraha</u>

2. _____ = supreme commander   _____

3. _____ = unquestionable ruler   _____

4. _____ = king of de:vatha:s   _____

5. _____ = king of demons   _____

6. _____ = controller of obstacles   _____

7. _____ = ruler of the worlds   _____

B. Add suffix 'ma:n' to get words which mean "to possess something" and make sentences.

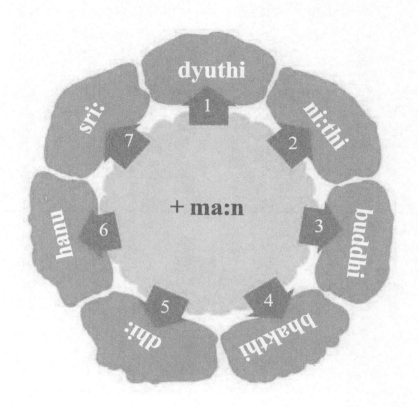

1. <u>dyuthima:n</u>   =   having effulgence   <u>Ra:ma is dyuthima:n</u>

2. _____   =   having morality   _____

3. _____   =   having wisdom   _____

4. _____   =   having devotion   _____

5. _____   =   possessing knowledge _____

6. _____   =   having swollen cheeks_____

7. _____   =   having wealth   _____

C. Add prefixes to word mukha:th to get 'words from someone'

guru		praptham	obtained from guru
thvan		srutham	heard from you
sri:	mukha:th	jna:tham	learnt from the letter
ve:da		jna:tham	learnt from the ve:das
bhavan		srutham	heard from you (addressing with respect)

Make sentences using the above phrases.

1. _____

2. _____

3. _____

4. _____

5. _____

D. Add suffix 'thru' to get some relationships and make sentences if possible.

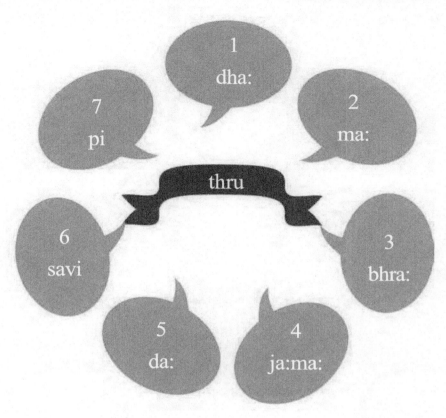

1. <u>dha:thru srushti</u>   = creation of Bramha <u>dha:thru srushti is amazing</u>.

2. _____ bhakthi   = devotion towards mother   _____

3. _____ sne:haha   = affinity of the brother   _____

4. _____ gauravaha   = respect towards son-in-law   _____

5. _____ hrudayam   = concern of the donor   _____

6. _____ mandalaha   = abode of sun   _____

7. _____ se:va   = service to father   _____

E. **Make words to know about 'possessing something' and make sentences**

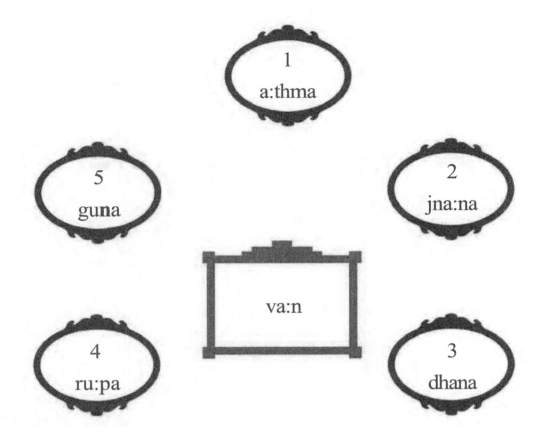

1. <u>a:thmava:n</u>   =   having good heart   <u>Si:tha is a:thmava:n.</u>

2. _____   =   having wisdom   _____

3. _____   =   having wealth   _____

4. _____   =   having good looks   _____

5. _____   =   having good manners   _____

XVII.   Reorder the below steps in order to reach supreme abode

1. Sathsang _____

2. Attaining the shape, size and qualities of Lord _____

3. Guidance from spiritual master _____

4. Realizing the need of spiritual master _____

5. Enjoy eternal bliss and do service to Him _____

6. Becomes "A:thmava:n" _____

7. Bath in Airamandam pond _____

8. Liberated soul crossing the 12 worlds _____

9. Gaining devotion and surrendering to God _____

10. Bath in the Viraja river _____

11. Keeping away from worldly desires _____

12. Lord relieving him from karmic bondages and guiding the soul to pass through Sushumna vein _____

13. Reaching the abode of Lord _____

14. Initiation of Ashta:kshari: manthra _____

15. Clear understanding of soul, nature and God _____

16. Touched by "Ama:nava" _____

17. Get divine body similar to Lord's divine body _____

XIX. Find 15 Differences

XX. Color this picture.

XXI. Color the sathsang activities.

XXII. What's wrong in the pictures below?

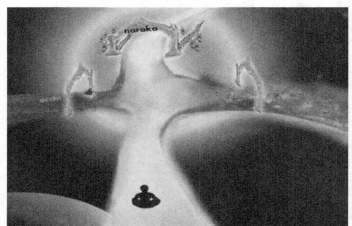

XXIII. Let us Practice- bhava nispruha

Do Service but do not help. Help is what we do feeling that we possess something and give that in charity; where as Service makes you feel that you have to do something whether you have it or not. You cannot stop from giving. Extending some kind of service is not for fame or recognition. Don't expect praises and if people praise don't feel proud.

If someone is in need, serve them. For example, if one needs a bone marrow or blood, donate or encourage others. Be part of it. Then they will feel happy. You too will feel happy seeing their happiness and satisfaction. Informing others about the service and inspiring them to participate is always good. Boasting that "I did it. Because of me, it happened…" is wrong.

XXIV. Project

Prepare a snakes and ladders game on a cardboard sheet that indicates the journey of a soul to Paramapadam.

Instructions

a.   Make a 10x10 squares table on the white drawing sheet (total of 100 squares).

b.   Mark numbers from 1 to 100 in those squares. Mark 1 as start and 100 as the destination abode of lord. (You can paste a picture of God on that 100th square)

c.   Write down the following good activities and few bad activities in the squares.

Good Activities	Bad Activities
1. Helping others	1. Eating junk food
2. Eating good food	2. Having jealousy
3. Not telling lies	3. Speaking lies
4. Worshipping parents/elders	4. Disobeying parents
5. Chanting Prajna slokas daily	5. Not attentive to teachers
6. Guidance from teacher	6. Stealing
7. Praying God	7. Hurting others

d. Draw ladders in squares with good activities and snakes in squares wi[th] bad activity in the above order. Draw taller ladders for the good activiti[es] with higher number in the above table. Draw in a similar pattern for snake[s]

e. Play the game with dice.

While playing realize how you reach God by doing good activities ar[d] how you fall down in this world again if you do bad activities.

XXV. **Food for thought**

Developing good qualities and practicing good activities always helps [us] to progress!

———◦◉◦———

Sarana:gathi
A Word of Submission

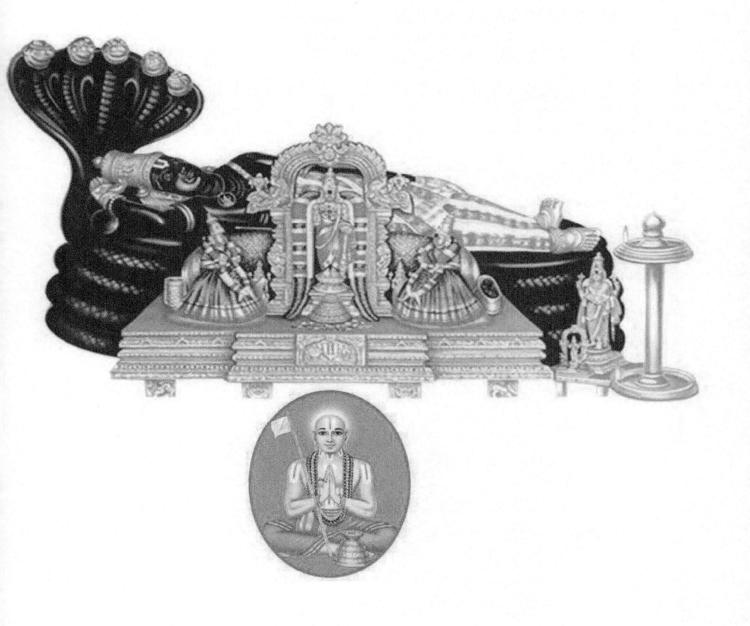

9. Sarana:gathi
A Word of Submission

I. True or False

1. Mother's throne is a garden of roses.

2. Lord Na:ra:yana runs the whole universe with great difficulty.

3. In this prayer, we surrender to the father of the whole universe.

II. Match the following

1.	Ma:tharam	a. possessor of all qualities – Mother Lakshmi
2.	Vibhava	b. possessor of all qualities – **Sri**:manna:ra:yana
3.	Guna	c. qualities
4.	Aiswarya	d. mother
5.	Bhagava:n	e. riches
6.	Bhagavathi:m	f. commandability
7.	Prapadye:	i. submit myself

III. Answer the following

1. Who are we surrendering to in this prayer?

   _____

2. What are the qualities of Mother Lakshmi?

   _____

3. Who is the lord of all the de:vathas?

   _____

4. Who wrote this prayer?

   _____

Yo:ga
Su:rya Namaska:rams

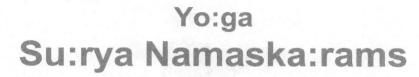

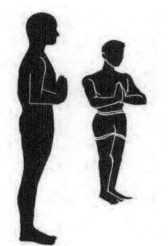

Do Su:rya Namaska:rams (Salutations to the Sun) for improving body, mind and life energy.

Postures to be observed

1.   Steps should be done slowly and gently. Fast, brisk movements are not recommended.

2.   Do Su:rya Namaska:rams on empty stomach.

3.   The preferred time is early in the morning or in the evening

4.   Focus on rhythmic, slow inhaling and exhaling.

Stthithi   Stand straight with both feet together and hands in namaska:ra posture.

Step 1.   As you breathe in, raise hands upwards. Slowly bend backward as per your comfort. Don't open your mouth.Breathe in as much as you can.

Step 2.   As you breathe out, slowly bend forward. Don't bend your knees. Bring your hands straight down. Palms should touch the ground on both sides of the feet. All fingers should be straight, pointing forward. Position of the palms and feet should be fixed such that till the last posture, their place is not moved.

Step 3. As you breathe in, extend your left leg backward. Bend yo[ur] left leg toes so that left knee touches the ground. Do not be[nd] your hands. Don't look upward or downward. Look f[or]ward.

Step 4. As you breathe out, extend your right leg back close to l[eft] leg. The whole body is like a straight plank. Vision should [be] straight.

Step 5. No Breathing.

For Men: Stretch fully on the ground. Only toes, knees, che[st] hands and forehead should touch the ground, no other p[art] should touch the ground. Angle both elbows towards t[he] body.

For Ladies: Squeeze in as if you are kneeling .Only to[es,] knees, hands and forehead touch the ground.

Step 6. As you breathe in, bend backward like an arc. Look towar[ds] the sky. Only toes and palms should touch the ground. Kne[es] shouldn't touch the ground. Mouth should be closed.

Step 7. As you breathe out, raise the middle part of your body, bending inwards. Your vision should be towards the navel. Raise your buttock. Both soles and palms should touch the ground.

Step 8. As you breathe in, bring the left leg to the original position, in between the hands. The right knee touches the ground and vision should be straight as in *Step 3*.

Step 9. As you breathe out, bring the second leg forward to the original position as in *Step 2*. Your fingers should point straight. Let your nose touch the knees. Don't bend your knees.

Step 10. Come to the normal position as in *Stthithi* as you breathe in.

This is one cycle. Repeat the same with right leg also.

There is a practise to chant a manthra before every cycle. Commonly chanted manthra are.

1. O:m mithra:ya namaha

2. O:m ravaye: namaha

3. O:m su:rya:ya namaha

4. O:m bha:nave: namaha

5. O:m khaga:ya namaha

6. O:m pushte: namaha

7. O:m hiraṇya na:bha:ya namaha

8. O:m mari:chaye: namaha

9. O:m a:dithya:ya namaha

10. O:m savithre: namaha

11. O:m arka:ya namaha

12. O:m bha:skara:ya namaha

LET US ENTER MODULE - 3

Printed in Great Britain
by Amazon